Probability

MATHEMATICS MONOGRAPH SERIES

EDITORS: **Robert Gunning,** *Princeton University;*
Hugo Rossi, *Brandeis University*

Frederick J. Almgren, Jr., *Princeton University*
PLATEAU'S PROBLEM: AN INVITATION TO VARIFOLD
GEOMETRY

John Lamperti, *Dartmouth College*
PROBABILITY: A SURVEY OF THE MATHEMATICAL THEORY

Robert T. Seeley, *Brandeis University*
AN INTRODUCTION TO FOURIER SERIES AND INTEGRALS

Michael Spivak, *Brandeis University*
CALCULUS ON MANIFOLDS: A MODERN APPROACH TO
CLASSICAL THEOREMS OF ADVANCED CALCULUS

John Lamperti

Dartmouth College

Probability

A SURVEY OF THE MATHEMATICAL THEORY

W. A. BENJAMIN, INC.

New York *Amsterdam*

1966

Probability: A Survey of the Mathematical Theory

Copyright © 1966 by W. A. Benjamin, Inc.

Library of Congress Catalog Card Number 66-28799
Manufactured in the United States of America

*The manuscript was put into production on June 6, 1966;
this volume was published on November 15, 1966*

W. A. BENJAMIN, INC.
New York, New York 10016

Editors' Foreword

Mathematics has been expanding in all directions at a fabulous rate during the past half century. New fields have emerged, the diffusion into other disciplines has proceeded apace, and our knowledge of the classical areas has grown ever more profound. At the same time, one of the most striking trends in modern mathematics is the constantly increasing interrelationship between its various branches. Thus the present-day students of mathematics are faced with an immense mountain of material. In addition to the traditional areas of mathematics as presented in the traditional manner—and these presentations do abound—there are the new and often enlightening ways of looking at these traditional areas, and also the vast new areas teeming with potentialities. Much of this new material is scattered indigestibly throughout the research journals, and frequently coherently organized only in the minds or unpublished notes of the working mathematicians. And students desperately need to learn more and more of this material.

This series of brief topical booklets has been conceived as a possible means to tackle and hopefully to alleviate some of these pedagogical problems. They are being written by active research mathematicians, who can look at the latest developments, who can use these developments to clarify and condense the required material, who know what ideas to underscore and what techniques to stress. We hope that these books will also serve to present to the able undergraduate an introduction to contemporary research and problems in mathematics, and that they will be sufficiently informal that the personal tastes and attitudes of the leaders in modern mathematics will shine through clearly to the readers.

Mathematical probability has by now come to be a part of most mathematical curricula, both pure and applied; and it is not uncommon to find an introduction to probability offered some time during the first two undergraduate years of mathematics. Dr. Lamperti's booklet provides a further exposure, to follow a course in measure theory by a rapid survey of mathematical probability at a moderately advanced level, before plunging more deeply into the advanced and special parts of the subject.

Robert Gunning
Hugo Rossi

Princeton, New Jersey
Waltham, Massachusetts
August 1966

Preface

On several occasions students in elementary probability courses who found the subject interesting have asked me for suggestions about further study. The first step, of course, should be to learn some measure theory, but I have not thought it obvious what to suggest after that. There have been, to be sure, excellent advanced treatises as well as monographs on special parts of the subject, but none has seemed entirely suitable for a person with little experience who wants a fast survey of the field. It is hoped that the present book will help to fill this gap, and that in addition it may serve the needs of more mature mathematicians who wish for a brief introduction to probability at a moderately advanced level.

This book is the outgrowth of a one-semester graduate course I have taught at Dartmouth College; the intent of the book, as of the course, is to provide a short survey of the main "classical" (i.e., before about 1950) lines of development in probability theory. Thus sums of independent random variables occupy at least half the text, and play a role in the final chapter on stochastic processes as well. Even so, the reader must not expect to "know" the theory of, for instance, "infinitely divisible laws" when he is finished; this aim would be inconsistent with the size of the book. It is hoped that he will have a good idea of what they are, know some facts about them, and have learned some of the methods of investigation which, when systematically applied, yield the rest of the story.

The formal prerequisite for this book is a fair working

knowledge of measure theory, approximately that provided in
H. Royden's recent text. (See the Bibliography at the end of
the book.) Some knowledge of elementary probability will
also be found very helpful; there is no better way to obtain
this than to read some of W. Feller's *Introduction* (Vol. 1).
In general, I have given complete definitions, but have provided no discussion as to why, for instance, independent
random variables are so interesting and important. On the
other hand, I have tried hard to motivate proofs and methods
of attack, avoiding the "rabbit from a hat" approach as far as
I could.

The measure-theoretic foundations are treated more briefly
than is usual. Theorems commonly found in real variable
texts are freely used, but are not proved here. My intention
is to provide what is needed in Chapter I, but no more than
the essentials, and then quickly get on with the story. In particular, the general theory of conditional probabilities and
expectations does not appear, as the subjects which really
require it could not be included. This book has, therefore, a
rather different flavor from others at about the same level, such
as the recent, good book by K. Krickeberg; the preferred
approach is ultimately a matter of taste rather than logical
necessity.

My historical references and credits are casual, perhaps too
much so; I have, I hope, always told the truth, but it is seldom
the whole truth. I apologize in advance to those who may
feel slighted, and ask that they consider my book as the result
of a quite informal course, rather than as a poor attempt at a
systematic treatise. I wish to state categorically that none of
the results presented in this book are my own, even when they
are not otherwise credited; the only possibilities for anything
original lie in the details of presentation and proofs. Finally,
I express my appreciation for the help of the students in my
course who prepared the lecture notes on which Chapters 2 and
3 are based, and for the cooperation of the Dartmouth Mathematics Department.

John Lamperti

Hanover, New Hampshire
August 1966

Contents

1

Foundations

1. PROBABILITY SPACES

Let Ω be any nonempty set, and suppose that $\mathfrak{B}$ is a *Borel field* (or σ field) of subsets of Ω. This means that $\mathfrak{B}$ is a collection of subsets which contains the empty set $\emptyset$ and is closed under the formation of complements and of the union of at most countably many of its members. Let P be a nonnegative function defined on $\mathfrak{B}$ such that $P(\Omega) = 1$ and satisfying

$$P(\bigcup_{n=1}^{\infty} A_n) = \sum_{n=1}^{\infty} P(A_n) \tag{1}$$

provided $A_n \in \mathfrak{B}$ and $A_n \cap A_m = \emptyset$ for each $n \neq m$. Then P is a *probability measure*, and the triple $(\Omega, \mathfrak{B}, P)$ is a *probability space*.

Problem 1. Let $\Omega = \{\omega_n\}$ be a countable set, and $\mathfrak{B}$ the collection of all its subsets. If $\{p_n\}$ is a sequence of nonnegative numbers whose sum is 1, let

$$P(S) = \sum_{\omega_n \in S} p_n \tag{2}$$

for any $S \subset \Omega$. Show that this defines a probability measure on $(\Omega, \mathfrak{B})$, and that, conversely, all such measures arise in this way.

More complicated measures are frequently obtained by means of the following "extension theorem." Suppose that $\mathfrak{F}$ is a *field* of subsets of Ω; that is, it is a collection of subsets containing $\emptyset$ and closed under complementation and the formation of *finite* unions. Let P be a nonnegative function on $\mathfrak{F}$ which is finitely additive,[1] has $P(\Omega) = 1$, and satisfies the following "continuity" condition:

$$\text{If} \qquad A_n \in \mathfrak{F}, \qquad A_{n+1} \subset A_n, \qquad \text{and} \qquad \bigcap_{n=1}^{\infty} A_n = \emptyset,$$
$$\text{then} \qquad \lim_{n \to \infty} P(A_n) = 0. \tag{3}$$

Let $\mathfrak{B} = \mathfrak{B}(\mathfrak{F})$ be the smallest Borel field containing all the members of $\mathfrak{F}$. (We sometimes say $\mathfrak{B}$ is *generated* by $\mathfrak{F}$.)

Theorem 1. *Under the above conditions, there is a unique probability measure on $\mathfrak{B}(\mathfrak{F})$ which is an extension of P.*

We will not prove this theorem, which can be found in many books on measure and integration theory. (For instance [R], Chapter 12, Section 2. The condition (3) appears there in a different, but equivalent, form; also see Problem 2 below.) In some works on probability—especially Kolmogorov's monograph [Ko]—the term "probability space" refers by definition to triples $(\Omega, \mathfrak{F}, P)$ satisfying the hypotheses of Theorem 1; in view of the existence of a unique extension there is no substantial difference between that usage and ours.

Problem 2. Show that the continuity condition (3) is equivalent to postulating that countable additivity holds whenever the union of disjoint sets in $\mathfrak{F}$ happens to belong to $\mathfrak{F}$ itself. Hence (3) is obviously a necessary condition for the extension of P to a measure.

The most familiar class of examples arises as follows: suppose that Ω is the real line and that $\mathfrak{B}$ is the field of all Borel sets. (That is, $\mathfrak{B}$ is the smallest σ field which contains all

---

[1] The property expressed in equation (1) is called "countable additivity."

open sets.) Given a measure P on $(\Omega, \mathfrak{B})$, the (point) function F defined by

$$F(x) = P(\{t \in R^1: -\infty < t \le x\}) \qquad (4)$$

is called the *distribution function* of P and is easily seen to have the following properties:

(i) F is nondecreasing;
(ii) F is continuous from the right;
(iii) $\lim_{x \to -\infty} F(x) = 0$ and $\lim_{x \to +\infty} F(x) = 1$.

Conversely, if we are given any distribution function F defined on R^1 (that is, a function satisfying (i), (ii), and (iii)), there is a unique measure P on Borel sets related to F by (4). To construct P, first define $\mathfrak{F}$ to be the field consisting of all finite unions of half-open intervals $(a, b]$ where $-\infty \le a < b \le +\infty$, and for each such interval let $P((a, b]) = F(b) - F(a)$. For a union of disjoint intervals, P is then defined by adding the values for the separate components; it is easy to see that the results are the same if a set in $\mathfrak{F}$ is represented as a disjoint union of intervals in two different ways. It is, of course, our hope to extend P as presently constituted to a genuine measure on $\mathfrak{B}$ by means of Theorem 1; to do so, condition (3) must be verified. (The other conditions are almost immediate.)

Problem 3. Prove that (3) holds in the above situation. (*Hint:* let A_n be a decreasing sequence of sets in $\mathfrak{F}$ such that $P(A_n) \nrightarrow 0$. Show that it is then possible to find closed sets $A_n' \subset A_n$ such that the sequence $\{A_n'\}$ has the finite-intersection property; the A_n' can be chosen to be uniformly bounded also. It follows that $\bigcap_{n=1}^{\infty} A_n$ is not empty.)

Problem 4. There is a simple alternative way to get the measure P, if we assume the existence of Lebesgue measure μ on $[0, 1]$. Let F be a distribution function which is continuous and strictly increasing, and define $P(A) = \mu(F(A))$ for any Borel set A. Show that P is a probability measure and that (4) holds. How should these statements be modified if F has jumps and level intervals?

Some authors require more of fields and measures before they bestow the title of "probability space." One common additional postulate is that of *completeness:* if $A \in \mathfrak{B}$, $P(A) = 0$, and $B \subset A$, then $B \in \mathfrak{B}$ also (and $P(B) = 0$). This is quite appealing to one's intuitive sense of "probability," and is harmless in the sense that any Borel field can be "completed" (with respect to a given measure P) in a simple and unique way. Moreover, the Caratheodory extension method (see [R]) leads automatically to complete spaces. There is only one disadvantage to this postulate: at times it may be necessary to consider several different probability measures on the same σ field, and although the completion of any one of them is well defined it may not be possible to find a single enlarged field on which the measures are simultaneously defined and complete. In any event, although most measures we will encounter are going to be complete we do not include completeness in the definition of a probability space.

Problem 5. Discuss the process of "completion." That is, if $(\Omega, \mathcal{B}, P)$ is a probability space show that there is a unique space $(\Omega, \mathcal{B}', P')$ which obeys the completeness axiom, satisfies the conditions that $\mathcal{B}' \supset \mathcal{B}$ and P' is an extension of P, and which is minimal with respect to these properties.

2. RANDOM VARIABLES AND EXPECTATIONS

Let $(\Omega, \mathcal{B}, P)$ be a probability space, and $X(\omega)$ a real-valued function on Ω. If X is measurable with respect to the field $\mathcal{B}$, that is, if the set $X^{-1}(S) \equiv \{\omega: X(\omega) \in S\}$ is a member of $\mathcal{B}$ for every Borel set S (equivalently open set, open interval, etc.) of the reals, then X is a *random variable*. It is possible to define the notion of a "Lebesgue integral" over any probability space (and more generally); the construction and basic properties of this integral are assumed to be known. (See any of the measure theory texts cited in the bibliography.) We will use the notation

$$E(X) = \int_{\Omega} X(\omega)\, dP \tag{1}$$

for this integral, and it will be called the *expected value* or *mean* of X. When we speak of $E(X)$ it is to be understood that the integral of $|X(\omega)|$ is finite; otherwise, the expectation does not exist.

It is important to notice that a random variable X on $(\Omega, \mathcal{B}, P)$ induces a probability measure P_X on R^1. The definition of this new measure for any Borel set S of reals is

$$P_X(S) = P(X^{-1}(S)). \tag{2}$$

The measure P_X is called the *distribution* of X; the point function F_X defined by

$$F_X(x) = P(\{\omega: X(\omega) \le x\}) \tag{3}$$

is called the *distribution function* of X and is clearly the same as the distribution function of P_X which was defined in Section 1. It will be necessary to know that expectations can be computed using P_X or F_X instead of the integral over Ω:

$$E(X) = \int_{R^1} x \, dP_X(x) = \int_{-\infty}^{\infty} x \, dF_X(x), \tag{4}$$

where the last expression is interpreted as an improper Riemann-Stieltjes integral, and the second as a Lebesgue-Stieltjes integral.

The first equality in (4) is a very special case of the following situation: Let $(\Omega', \mathfrak{B}')$ be any space together with a Borel field of subsets, and suppose the mapping $\phi\colon \Omega \to \Omega'$ is measurable in the sense that $\phi^{-1}(M) \in \mathfrak{B}$ for each $M \in \mathfrak{B}'$. Define a measure P_ϕ on $\mathfrak{B}'$ by setting

$$P_\phi(M) = P(\phi^{-1}(M)) \tag{5}$$

for all $M \in \mathfrak{B}'$, and let X' be a measurable function from $(\Omega', \mathfrak{B}')$ to the reals.

Theorem 1. *The composite function $X(\omega) = X'[\phi(\omega)]$ is a random variable on $(\Omega, \mathfrak{B}, P)$, and*

$$E(X) = \int_{\Omega'} X' \, dP_\phi \tag{6}$$

holds, where the existence of either side implies that of the other.

Proof. The measurability of X is obvious. Suppose that X' is the characteristic function of a set $A \in \mathfrak{B}'$. Then the right side of (6) is just $P_\phi(A)$. But X is also a characteristic function, that of $\phi^{-1}(A)$, so that $E(X) = P(\phi^{-1}(A))$. In view of the definition (5) these are equal, so (6) holds for characteristic functions. The extension to finite linear combinations—simple functions—follows very easily.

Suppose next that $X' \ge 0$. There then exists an increasing sequence of simple functions X'_n which tend to X', and by the monotone convergence theorem we have

$$\lim_{n \to \infty} \int_{\Omega'} X'_n \, dP_\phi = \int_{\Omega'} X' \, dP_\phi. \tag{7}$$

But the composites $X_n(\omega) = X'_n[\phi(\omega)]$ are simple functions too, and as they increase to X we have

$$\lim_{n \to \infty} E(X_n) = E(X). \tag{8}$$

Since we have seen that (6) holds for the simple functions X_n and X'_n, it follows from (7) and (8) that (6) also holds for X and X'.

Finally, the argument above can be applied separately to the positive and negative parts of X', to establish (6) in the general case when $X' \geq 0$ does not hold. It should be clear from our proof that $E(X)$ exists if and only if X' is integrable with respect to P_ϕ.

Problem 1. Explain how (4) follows from Theorem 1, and verify that if f is any Borel function on the reals, then

$$E(f(X)) = \int_{R^1} f(x) \, dP_X \tag{9}$$

provided either side exists.

Many of the usual definitions of convergence of a sequence of functions play important roles in probability theory, but it is customary to disguise them with new names. If $X_n(\omega)$ is a sequence of random variables defined on a probability space $(\Omega, \mathfrak{B}, P)$ such that the set $\{\omega : \lim_{n \to \infty} X_n(\omega) \text{ exists}\}$ has P measure equal to 1, it is said that X_n *converges almost surely* (abbreviated a.s.); this, of course, is the same as the usual "convergence almost everywhere."

Problem 2. Show that if X_n converges a.s., the function $X(\omega)$ which equals $\lim X_n$ when it exists and (say) 0 otherwise will automatically be a random variable.

The concept of convergence of X_n to X in measure becomes in our setting

$$\lim_{n \to \infty} P(\{\omega : |X_n(\omega) - X(\omega)| > \epsilon\}) = 0 \tag{10}$$

for each $\epsilon > 0$, and we will always call this *convergence in probability*. Finally, if for some $p > 0$

$$\lim_{n \to \infty} E(|X_n - X|^p) = 0, \tag{11}$$

we have *convergence in the mean* of order p. It is not difficult to see that either convergence a.s. or in the mean (of any order) implies convergence in probability, and that there is no other implication among the different modes. All three of them will be used in Chapter 2 in connection with "laws of large numbers."

Problem 3. Verify the next-to-last sentence.

We conclude this section with a brief mention of another axiom sometimes imposed on the notion of a probability space— the requirement that the space be *perfect*. We have discussed the measure P_X induced on Borel sets of the real line by a random variable X; it was defined in (2). P can always be completed in the manner of Problem 1.5, and in the process P_X is defined on a certain σ field larger than that of all Borel sets. The measure P_X on *this* field can be completely reconstructed from the distribution function $F_X(x) = P(X \leq x)$. However, there is no reason why P_X may not be defined by (2) for still more sets if the field $\mathfrak{B}$ is rich enough; a perfect measure is one for which this does not occur for any random variable. This axiom is discussed and used in [GK] (among others), and an appendix by J. L. Doob added to the English translation is well worth reading for a general discussion of several foundation questions as well as for notes on perfect measures.

Again, as with completeness, most measures we are going to look at will be perfect. But we will not assume "perfection," nor stop to verify it even when it holds in some special case. Instead we will usually take the point of view that if X is a random variable, $P(X \in A)$ will be of interest only for those sets A whose P_X measure is determined by the distribution function of X, and the question of $\mathfrak{B}$ measurability of $\{\omega : X(\omega) \in A\}$ for any other sets A will be ignored.

3. INDEPENDENCE

Let $(\Omega, \mathfrak{B}, P)$ be any probability space, and let $A_1, \ldots, A_n$ be "events"; that is, sets belonging to $\mathfrak{B}$. The events are called *independent* if every subcollection of them satisfies

$$P(A_{i_1} \cap A_{i_2} \cap \cdots \cap A_{i_k}) = P(A_{i_1})P(A_{i_2}) \cdots P(A_{i_k}). \quad (1)$$

If $X_1, \ldots, X_n$ are random variables on the space, they will be called independent provided the events $A_i = \{\omega: X_i(\omega) \in S_i\}$ satisfy (1) for every choice of linear Borel sets $S_1, \ldots, S_n$. For infinite collections of events or of random variables, countable or not, independence holds by definition provided every finite subset is independent. As Kolmogorov and others have remarked, it is the concept of independence more than anything else which has given probability theory a life of its own, distinct from other branches of analysis.

Further basic discussion of the independence of "large" sets of random variables will be given in Section 10; the rest of this section deals mostly with only two variables at a time. If X and Y are any pair of random variables, independent or not, they generate a mapping $Z(\omega) = (X(\omega), Y(\omega))$ from Ω into R^2. This mapping is Borel measurable (Problem 1 below) and so a measure $P_{X,Y}$ is induced by it on the field of planar Borel sets. This measure is called the *joint distribution* of X and Y, and

$$F_{X,Y}(x, y) = P(\{\omega: X(\omega) \leq x \text{ and } Y(\omega) \leq y\}) \qquad (2)$$

is their *joint distribution function*. The measure $P_{X,Y}$ can be reconstructed from $F_{X,Y}$ in essentially the same way as that outlined in Section 1 for one dimension. These remarks generalize immediately to the case of n random variables.

Problem 1. Show that $Z^{-1}(S) \epsilon \mathcal{B}$ for every Borel set S in R^2.

If the random variables X and Y of the previous paragraph are independent, then it follows from the definition that $P_{X,Y}$ is a *product measure*. This simply means that for every pair of linear Borel sets R, S, we have

$$P_{X,Y}(R \times S) = P_X(R)P_Y(S), \qquad (3)$$

where $R \times S$ is the set of points in R^2 with x coordinate in R and y coordinate in S. In particular, the joint distribution function of X and Y is the product of their individual distribution functions.

Problem 2. Prove the converse of the last assertion; that is, show that if

$$F_{X,Y}(x,y) = F_X(x)F_Y(y) \qquad \text{for all } x, y,$$

then X and Y are independent.

We turn to a fact which will be used repeatedly.

Theorem 1. *Let X and Y be independent random variables. Then $E(XY)$ exists if both $E(X)$ and $E(Y)$ do and in that case*

$$E(XY) = E(X)E(Y). \tag{4}$$

Conversely if $E(XY)$ exists and neither X nor Y vanishes a.s., then $E(X)$ and $E(Y)$ exist also.

Proof. Suppose first that both X and Y are simple functions, that is, that there are two families of disjoint sets $\{A_i\}$ and $\{B_i\}$ and of distinct numbers $\{a_i\}$ and $\{b_i\}$ such that

$$X(\omega) = \sum_{i=1}^{n} a_i \phi_{A_i}(\omega) \qquad \text{and} \qquad Y(\omega) = \sum_{i=1}^{m} b_i \phi_{B_i}(\omega).\,^2 \tag{5}$$

From the definition of independence we infer that

$$P(A_i \cap B_j) = P(A_i)P(B_j) \tag{6}$$

for each i and j, and (4) follows easily:

$$E(XY) = E\left\{\sum_i a_i\phi_{A_i} \sum_j b_j\phi_{B_j}\right\} = E\left\{\sum_{i,j} a_i b_j \phi_{A_i \cap B_j}\right\}$$
$$= \sum_{i,j} a_i b_j P(A_i \cap B_j) = \sum_i a_i P(A_i) \sum_j b_j P(B_j)$$
$$= E(X)E(Y).$$

Of course, the expectations necessarily exist for simple functions.

Now, let X and Y be nonnegative and independent, but not necessarily simple. Define

$$X_n(\omega) = \begin{cases} \dfrac{i}{2^n} & \text{if } \dfrac{i}{2^n} \leq X(\omega) < \dfrac{i+1}{2^n}, \\ & \qquad\qquad i = 0, 1, \ldots, n2^n, \\ 0, & \text{otherwise}, \end{cases} \tag{7}$$

and define Y_n similarly in terms of Y. Then X_n and Y_n are simple, and because it is obvious that they are independent we have

$$E(X_n Y_n) = E(X_n)E(Y_n) \tag{8}$$

for each n. But our construction of X_n insures also that $X_n(\omega) \nearrow X(\omega)$ for each ω, and so it follows from the monotone

---

² By $\phi_A(\omega)$ we mean the function which is 1 if $\omega \in A$ and 0 if $\omega \notin A$, where A is any subset of Ω.

convergence theorem that

$$\lim_{n \to \infty} E(X_n) = E(X). \tag{9}$$

The same things are of course true for Y_n and Y and for $X_n Y_n$ and XY, and together with (8) they yield (4). The "existence if and only if" also is a consequence of the monotone convergence theorem in this case: if $E(XY) < \infty$ both $E(X_n)$ and $E(Y_n)$ must be bounded unless one or the other is always zero.

Finally, we must remove the restriction to nonnegative X and Y. Let $X^+(\omega) = \max \{X(\omega), 0\}$ and $X^-(\omega) = \max \{-X(\omega), 0\}$, so that $X = X^+ - X^-$ for each $\omega \in \Omega$; do the same for Y. It is easy to check that $X^\pm$ and $Y^\pm$ are still independent, and since they are also nonnegative we know that (4) holds for them. If $E(X)$ and $E(Y)$ exist, then $E(X^\pm)$ and $E(Y^\pm)$ exist too and we have

$$
\begin{aligned}
E(XY) &= E\{(X^+ - X^-)(Y^+ - Y^-)\} \\
&= E(X^+Y^+) - E(X^-Y^+) - E(X^+Y^-) + E(X^-Y^-) \\
&= E(X^+)E(Y^+) - E(X^-)E(Y^+) - E(X^+)E(Y^-) \\
&\qquad\qquad\qquad\qquad\qquad + E(X^-)E(Y^-) \\
&= \{E(X^+) - E(X^-)\}\{E(Y^+) - E(Y^-)\} \\
&\qquad\qquad\qquad\qquad\qquad = E(X)E(Y).
\end{aligned}
$$

In this process we have exhibited XY as a sum of four random variables with expectations, so $E(XY)$ must exist.

If instead it is supposed that XY has an expectation, so do $(XY)^+$ and $(XY)^-$. But $(XY)^+ = X^+Y^+ + X^-Y^-$ and $(XY)^- = X^+Y^- + X^-Y^+$, so that the four quantities $E(X^\pm Y^\pm)$ exist. Suppose $E(X)$ does not exist. Then $E(X^+) = \infty$ or $E(X^-) = \infty$; assume the former. Since both $E(X^+Y^+)$ and $E(X^+Y^-)$ are finite, by the argument above for the nonnegative case both $E(Y^+)$ and $E(Y^-) = 0$ and so $Y = 0$ a.s. The case $E(X^-) = \infty$ is handled similarly; this completes the proof.

Problem 3. Construct another proof of Theorem 1 based on the relation

$$E(XY) = \int_{R^2} xy \, dP_{X,Y}. \tag{10}$$

(Use Fubini's theorem. Equation (10) is a special case of Theorem 2.1 with R^2 as Ω' and the function xy in the role of X'.)

Problem 4. Use either of the two approaches above to show that if $X_1, \ldots, X_n$ are independent with finite means, then

$$E\left(\prod_{i=1}^{n} X_i\right) = \prod_{i=1}^{n} E(X_i). \tag{11}$$

(*Note:* It is tempting to proceed as follows ($n = 3$):

$$E(X_1 X_2 X_3) = E(X_1)E(X_2 X_3) = E(X_1)E(X_2)E(X_3).$$

The trouble is that we have not shown X_1 and $X_2 X_3$ to be independent. This approach will be justified as a by-product of results in Section 10 below, but in the meantime we will use (11) with $n = 3$, 4 in Section 7.)

Much of "classical" probability theory—and much of this book—is concerned with sums of two or more independent random variables. It is clear that the distribution of such a sum is determined by the distributions of the individual variables; our next result shows how.

Theorem 2. *Let X and Y be independent random variables, having distribution functions F and G respectively. Then the distribution of their sum is given by*

$$P(X + Y \leq x) = \int_{-\infty}^{\infty} F(x - y)\,dG(y)$$
$$= \int_{-\infty}^{\infty} G(x - y)\,dF(y). \tag{12}$$

Proof. Define the function

$$f(r, s) = \begin{cases} 1 & \text{if } r + s \leq x, \\ 0, & \text{otherwise;} \end{cases} \tag{13}$$

clearly, f is a Borel-measurable function on R^2. Applying Theorem 2.1 with R^2 as Ω' and $\phi(\omega) = (X(\omega), Y(\omega))$, we have at once

$$E\{f(X, Y)\} = \int_{R^2} f\,dP_{X,Y}. \tag{14}$$

The left side, of course, is just $P(X + Y \leq x)$. Since $P_{X,Y}$ is a product measure (independence), Fubini's theorem can be used to express the right side of (14) as an iterated integral in either of two ways:

$$\int_{R^2} f\,dP_{X,Y} = \int \left\{\int f(r, s)P_X(dr)\right\} P_Y(ds)$$
$$= \int \left\{\int f(r, s)P_Y(ds)\right\} P_X(dr). \tag{15}$$

These two expressions are the same as the two Lebesgue-Stieltjes integrals in (12), and so the theorem is proved.

Corollary. *Suppose that the distribution of X is absolutely continuous, so that $F(x) = \int_{-\infty}^{x} f(u)\, du$ for some density [3] f. Then the distribution of $X + Y$ is also absolutely continuous, and its density is* (a.e.) *given by*

$$\frac{d}{dx} P(X + Y \leq x) = \int_{-\infty}^{\infty} f(x - y)\, dG(y). \qquad (16)$$

Proof. By Fubini's theorem we have

$$\int_{-\infty}^{x} \left\{ \int_{-\infty}^{\infty} f(t - y)\, dG(y) \right\} dt = \int_{-\infty}^{\infty} \left\{ \int_{-\infty}^{x} f(t - y)\, dt \right\} dG(y)$$
$$= \int_{-\infty}^{\infty} F(x - y)\, dG(y).$$

The result is $P(X + Y \leq x)$ by (12), and so we have exhibited this distribution as the integral of the right-hand side of (16).

Remark. By means of these results, many of the facts about sums of independent random variables could be rephrased as statements about the *convolution* of measures or distribution functions on R^1. This situation suggests that Fourier analysis will be an important tool for the study of such sums; that this idea is correct will, I hope, be amply demonstrated in Chapter 3.

Finally, this seems a reasonable place for some comments on conditional probabilities. If $(\Omega, \mathcal{B}, P)$ is a probability space, $A \in \mathcal{B}$, and $P(A) > 0$, we call

$$P(B|A) \equiv \frac{P(A \cap B)}{P(A)} \qquad (17)$$

the conditional probability of B given A; clearly, $P(B|A) = P(B)$ if and only if B and A are independent events. The set function $P(\cdot|A)$ is itself a probability measure on $(\Omega, \mathcal{B})$ and so determines a *conditional expectation* which we define by

$$E(X|A) = \int_{\Omega} X(\omega) P(d\omega|A). \qquad (18)$$

---

[3] This phrase defines a *probability density;* it is clear that any nonnegative function on R^1 with integral one is the density of some distribution.

All of our discussion of properties of random variables, etc., carries over to the new (conditional) probability space. For instance, we can define *conditional independence* of events or random variables by applying the previous definition with the new measure. The reader is assumed to be somewhat familiar with the intuitive meaning of these notions.

The situation above, with $P(A) > 0$, is the elementary case. More general theories define conditional probabilities or expectations with respect to a random variable, or to a sub-Borel field of ⑬. ($P(B|A)$, where A is a single event with $P(A) = 0$, can not be given a useful unique meaning in general.) We will not discuss these matters in this book, and even the elementary case will be mentioned infrequently—hardly at all in Chapters 2 and 3. The general theory of conditional expectations does play a vital role in the study of stochastic processes, and the reader wishing to go beyond the introduction provided by Chapter 4 might well make it his next item of business.

4. THE CONSTRUCTION OF RANDOM VARIABLES

Most of the results in Chapters 2 and 3 below are of the following form: "If $X_1, X_2, \ldots$ are independent random variables whose distribution functions are $F_1, F_2, \ldots$, then . . . ." The question arises as to whether, given the distributions F_n, a probability space $(\Omega, \text{⑬}, P)$ really exists on which such a family of random variables (abbreviated r.v.'s) can be defined. If not, our theorems, though still true, certainly lose some interest! The affirmative answer to this question can be most easily obtained by the construction of product measures; the number of factors which can be "multiplied" need not even be countable.

A more general problem occurs when the r.v.'s are not assumed to be independent. In this case, instead of a single sequence of distributions F_n it is necessary to specify the joint distribution of each finite subset of the X's. Kolmogorov has shown that if some simple consistency conditions hold, a suitable probability space can always be found. We proceed to discuss the construction.[4]

---

[4] Only the case of product measure is needed before Section 23; the reader not troubled by the simpler question in the first paragraph above may wish to defer reading the rest of this section until then.

Let us first obtain the necessary conditions. If $\{X_\alpha, \alpha \in \mathcal{Q}\}$ is a family (not necessarily countable; $\mathcal{Q}$ is any index set) of r.v.'s on $(\Omega, \mathcal{B}, P)$, we denote their *joint distributions* by

$$P_{\alpha_1, \ldots, \alpha_n}(S) = P(\phi^{-1}_{\alpha_1, \ldots, \alpha_n}(S)), \tag{1}$$

where S is any Borel set in R^n and $\phi_{\alpha_1, \ldots, \alpha_n}$ is that mapping from Ω into R^n sending ω into the point with coordinates $(X_{\alpha_1}(\omega), \ldots, X_{\alpha_n}(\omega))$. Thus what must be specified is a probability measure $P_{\alpha_1, \ldots, \alpha_n}$ on the Borel sets of R^n corresponding to each ordered finite subset $(\alpha_1, \ldots, \alpha_n)$ of $\mathcal{Q}$.

Let π denote a permutation of the integers $1, \ldots, n$, and let f_π be that one to one map of R^n onto itself which takes $(x_1, \ldots, x_n)$ into $(x_{\pi 1}, \ldots, x_{\pi n})$. It is clear that

$$\phi_{\alpha_{\pi 1}, \ldots, \alpha_{\pi n}}(\omega) = f_\pi(\phi_{\alpha_1, \ldots, \alpha_n}(\omega)),$$

and so the distributions $P_{\alpha_1, \ldots, \alpha_n}$ defined in (1) must satisfy

$$P_{\alpha_{\pi 1}, \ldots, \alpha_{\pi n}}(S) = P_{\alpha_1, \ldots, \alpha_n}(f_\pi^{-1}(S)). \tag{2}$$

This is the first consistency condition on the joint distributions.

Suppose next that $\sigma_{n+m, n}$ is the projection map from R^{n+m} to R^n which sends $(x_1, \ldots, x_{n+m}) \in R^{n+m}$ into $(x_1, \ldots, x_n) \in R^n$. Let S be any Borel set in R^n, and put $\hat{S} = \sigma^{-1}_{n+m, n}(S)$. (Thus $\hat{S}$ contains those points in R^{n+m} whose first n coordinates determine a point in S.) If $(\alpha_1, \ldots, \alpha_{n+m})$ is any ordered set of $n + m$ "parameter values," clearly,

$$\phi^{-1}_{\alpha_1, \ldots, \alpha_n}(S) = \phi^{-1}_{\alpha_1, \ldots, \alpha_{n+m}}(\hat{S}),$$

and so by (1) we must have

$$P_{\alpha_1, \ldots, \alpha_n}(S) = P_{\alpha_1, \ldots, \alpha_{n+m}}(\sigma^{-1}_{n+m, n}(S)). \tag{3}$$

This is the second condition. Both conditions, as we have seen, are for rather superficial reasons necessarily satisfied by the system of joint distributions of any family $\{X_\alpha\}$ of random variables. We shall now see that they are sufficient for the existence of such a family:

Theorem 1 (Kolmogorov). *Let $\mathcal{Q}$ be any set, and let $P_{\alpha_1, \ldots, \alpha_n}$ be a Borel probability measure on R^n for each finite ordered subset of $\mathcal{Q}$. Assume that this family of measures $\{P_{\alpha_1, \ldots, \alpha_n}\}$ satisfies conditions (2) and (3). Then there exists a probability space*

$(\Omega, \mathcal{B}, P)$ *and random variables* $\{X_\alpha, \alpha \in \mathcal{A}\}$ *defined on it such that condition* (1) *holds for all finite subsets* $(\alpha_1, \ldots, \alpha_n)$.

Proof. We will use a direct product to define our measurable space, although of course we do not want product measure except in the special case when the random variables are to be independent. Accordingly, let

$$\Omega = \prod_{\alpha \in \mathcal{A}} R_\alpha \qquad (R_\alpha \text{ the real line}) \qquad (4)$$

be the space of all functions from $\mathcal{A}$ to the reals. A typical element of Ω will be denoted $\omega = \omega(\alpha)$. We confide at the outset that the random variables under construction are going to be the "coordinate functions" defined by

$$X_\alpha(\omega) = \omega(\alpha). \qquad (5)$$

Let $(\alpha_1, \ldots, \alpha_n)$ be any ordered finite subset of $\mathcal{A}$, and S any Borel subset of R^n. The set

$$\{\omega \in \Omega: (\omega(\alpha_1), \ldots, \omega(\alpha_n)) \in S\} = \phi_{\alpha_1, \ldots, \alpha_n}^{-1}(S) \quad (6)$$

is called a *Borel cylinder set*. Here $\phi_{\alpha_1, \ldots, \alpha_n}$ has the same meaning as before; namely, it sends $\omega = \omega(\alpha)$ into the point in R^n with coordinates $(X_{\alpha_1}(\omega), \ldots, X_{\alpha_n}(\omega))$. It is not difficult to see that the family of all Borel cylinder sets forms a finitely additive field $\mathcal{F}$; let $\mathcal{B}$ denote the smallest σ field of subsets of Ω which contains $\mathcal{F}$. Our method will be to define a measure P on $\mathcal{F}$ and extend it to $\mathcal{B}$ by Theorem 1.1.

Problem 1. Verify that $\mathcal{F}$ is a field.

It is clear how to begin; for the set described in (6) we must define

$$P(\phi_{\alpha_1, \ldots, \alpha_n}^{-1}(S)) = P_{\alpha_1, \ldots, \alpha_n}(S) \qquad (7)$$

in order to have the correct distributions for our random variables. (That is, we must make sure (1) holds.) The first thing to be verified is that this definition is nonambiguous; this is where the consistency conditions (2) and (3) are required. Suppose that two cylinder sets C and D are defined by

$$C = \phi_{\alpha_1, \ldots, \alpha_n}^{-1}(S), \qquad D = \phi_{\beta_1, \ldots, \beta_m}^{-1}(S'), \qquad (8)$$

where S and S' are respectively Borel sets in R^n and R^m. If $(\gamma_1, \ldots, \gamma_k)$ is some ordering of the parameter values in $\{\alpha_i\} \cup \{\beta_j\}$, then both C and D can be equally well described by means of

$$C = \phi^{-1}_{\gamma_1, \ldots, \gamma_k}(T), \qquad D = \phi^{-1}_{\gamma_1, \ldots, \gamma_k}(T'), \qquad (9)$$

where T and T' are now Borel sets in R^k. Moreover, the change from (8) to (9) is effected simply by an inverse of the "projection" from R^k into R^n or R^m, plus a reordering of the indices γ_i. Thus, because of (2) and (3), the measure ascribed to C (or D) by (7) will be the same regardless of whether C (or D) is defined by (8) or (9). It only remains to observe that if $C = D$ then $T = T'$ in (9), and so the definition (7) applied to either of the two representations of $C = D$ in (8) must yield the same result.

Problem 2. Show that the measure P defined on $\mathfrak{F}$ by (7) is finitely additive.

In order to apply Theorem 1.1, it is still necessary to verify the continuity condition (1.3). The proof is a bit similar to that used in one dimension (in Problem 1.3). Let $C_1 \supset C_2 \supset C_3 \cdots$ be any decreasing sequence of Borel cylinder sets (members of $\mathfrak{F}$) with $P(C_n) \to \delta > 0$; we will show that $\bigcap_{n=1}^{\infty} C_n \neq \emptyset$. Recall that each cylinder set C_n is defined by (6) using a finite set $\mathfrak{a}^{(n)} = (\alpha_1^{(n)}, \ldots, \alpha_k^{(n)})$ of parameters $(k = k(n))$ and a Borel set $S_n \subset R^k$. There is no loss of generality in assuming that the sets $\mathfrak{a}^{(n)}$ are increasing.

There is also no loss in assuming S_n compact. To see this, note that a set $S'_n \subset S_n$ which *is* compact can always be chosen with

$$P_{\alpha_1^{(n)}, \ldots, \alpha_k^{(n)}}(S_n - S'_n) \leq \frac{\delta}{2 \cdot 2^n}.$$

If $C'_n = \phi^{-1}_{\alpha_1^{(n)}, \ldots, \alpha_k^{(n)}}(S'_n)$, we then have

$$P(C_n - C'_n) \leq \frac{\delta}{2 \cdot 2^n};$$

the only trouble is that the sets C'_n may not be decreasing. Finally, therefore, we let $C''_n = C'_1 \cap \cdots \cap C'_n$. These sets are decreasing, are derived (by means of $\phi^{-1}_{\alpha_1^{(n)}, \ldots, \alpha_k^{(n)}}$) from compact sets S_n'' in R^k, and they also satisfy

$$P(C_n'') \to \delta' > 0,$$

since in fact

$$P(C_n'') \ge P(C_n) - \sum_{i=1}^{n} P(C_i - C_i') \ge \frac{\delta}{2}. \tag{10}$$

Hence we can, as stated, assume that our cylinders have compact bases.

Problem 3. Verify (10).

We are almost ready to exhibit a point in $\overset{\infty}{\underset{n=1}{\cap}} C_n$. For each n choose some $\omega_n \in C_n$. By the definition of C_1, the point whose coordinates are $(\omega_1(\alpha_1^{(1)}), \ldots, \omega_1(\alpha_{k(1)}^{(1)}))$ belongs to S_1 which is a compact set in R_k; if we replace ω_1 by ω_m with $m > 1$ we still find that $(\omega_m(\alpha_1^{(1)}), \ldots, \omega_m(\alpha_k^{(1)})) \in S_1$ since $C_m \subset C_1$. Hence, we can choose a subsequence n' such that the sequence of vectors $(\omega_{n'}(\alpha_1^{(1)}), \ldots, \omega_{n'}(\alpha_k^{(1)}))$ is convergent. We then choose a subsubsequence which also converges for the larger set of parameter values $\{\alpha_1^{(2)}, \ldots, \alpha_{k(2)}^{(2)}\}$, and so on. Finally, by the "diagonal argument," we obtain a single sequence $\{\omega_n^*\}$ such that

$$\lim_{n \to \infty} \omega_n^*(\alpha_j^{(i)}) = x_j^{(i)} \tag{11}$$

exists for each parameter value $\alpha_j^{(i)}$ which occurs in the definition of one of the cylinder sets C_i. Let us denote the (countable) set of such values by $\mathcal{C}_0$.

Define an element $\omega_0 \in \Omega$ by setting

$$\omega_0(\alpha) = \begin{cases} x_j^{(i)} & \text{if } \alpha = \alpha_j^{(i)} \in \mathcal{C}_0, \\ 0, & \text{otherwise.} \end{cases} \tag{12}$$

(The choice of ω_0 for $\alpha \notin \mathcal{C}_0$ is arbitrary.) We shall see that $\omega_0 \in \overset{\infty}{\underset{n=1}{\cap}} C_n$. In fact, recall that

$$C_n = \{\omega: (\omega(\alpha_1^{(n)}), \ldots, \omega(\alpha_k^{(n)})) \in S_n\}.$$

But by construction the vector $(x_1^{(n)}, \ldots, x_k^{(n)})$ is the limit of points in S_n and so itself is in S_n by compactness; hence

$\omega_0 \in C_n$ for each n. This verifies that $\bigcap_{n=1}^{\infty} C_n$ is not empty, so that (1.3) does indeed hold. Theorem 1.1 does the rest; the proof is complete.

Corollary. *Suppose that* $F_1, F_2, \ldots$ *is a sequence of probability distribution functions. Then there exists a probability space* $(\Omega, \mathfrak{B}, P)$ *with independent random variables* $X_1, X_2, \ldots$ *defined on it such that the distribution function of* X_n *is* F_n.

Proof. Given a finite subset of indices $(i_1, \ldots, i_n)$, we choose the joint distribution $P_{i_1, \ldots, i_n}$ on R^n to be the product of the n measures on R^1 determined by the distribution functions $F_{i_1}, \ldots, F_{i_n}$. It is pretty obvious that (2) and (3) are satisfied, so Theorem 1 can be applied; the random variables which it provides then satisfy the conclusion of the corollary.

Remarks. This proof has the flaw that it assumes knowledge of product measure for a finite number of factors. The case of two factors is discussed in [R]; the general case in [H]. But as we have commented in Section 3, in Euclidean spaces there is another approach: the (multidimensional) distribution function (abbreviated d.f.) of the desired product measure is just the product of the one-dimensional d.f.'s, and the construction of a measure from its d.f. can be done in R^n much as in R^1. A more systematic treatment of all these matters is given in [Kr]. Incidentally, a fact worth knowing is that Kolmogorov's theorem cannot be proved without some appeal to considerations going beyond measure theory (we used the local compactness of R^n), but that the product measure corresponding to any collection of probability spaces can be constructed.

Problem 4. Suppose that each F_n is of the form

$$F_n(x) = \begin{cases} 0 & \text{for } x < 0, \\ \frac{1}{2} & \text{for } 0 \le x < 1, \\ 1 & \text{for } x \ge 1. \end{cases} \tag{13}$$

Show that the space $(\Omega, \mathfrak{B}, P)$ which results from the construction above has a natural correspondence (defined almost everywhere) with the unit interval, under which P goes over into Lebesgue measure.

2

Laws of Large Numbers and Series

5. THE WEAK LAW OF LARGE NUMBERS

The classical theorem about "Bernoulli trials" can be stated as follows: For each n, let $X_1, \ldots, X_n$ be independent random variables on some probability space such that X_i takes only the values 1 and 0, with probability p and $q = 1 - p$ respectively.[1] Then for each $\epsilon > 0$,

$$\lim_{n \to \infty} P\left(\left| \frac{X_1 + \cdots + X_n}{n} - p \right| > \epsilon \right) = 0. \qquad (1)$$

A proof (see [F]) which is very direct and elementary can be based on the particular features of the "binomial distribution"

$$P(X_1 + \cdots + X_n = k) = \binom{n}{k} p^k q^{n-k}. \qquad (2)$$

However, simple methods of vastly greater generality were developed in the latter part of the 19th century by the Russian

[1] It is possible, but not necessary, to define all the random variables $X_1, X_2, \ldots$ on the same probability space. If this is not done finite spaces can be used, that for $X_1, \ldots, X_n$ requiring 2^n points.

mathematician P. L. Chebyshev [2] which we will now describe.

If X is any random variable, the quantities $m_k = E(X^k)$, if they exist, are called the *moments* of X. In particular, the first moment m_1 is simply the mean of X, and the second moment of $X - m_1$ is called the *variance* of X and formally defined by

$$\sigma^2 = \operatorname{var}(X) = E(\{X - E(X)\}^2); \tag{3}$$

the square root σ of the variance is the *standard deviation*. It is easy to see that $\sigma^2 = m_2 - m_1^2$.

Problem 1. Show that m_k exists if and only if $E(\{X - a\}^k)$ exists for some a ($k \geq 0$), and also that if m_k exists for some $k > 0$ so does m_j for every $0 \leq j \leq k$ and

$$m_j \leq E(|X|^k)^{j/k}.$$

It is possible to compute the integer order moments of a sum of independent random variables in terms of the moments of the summands, and this provides an approach to many important theorems. The situation is especially simple for the first moment and the variance, which are both additive. In the case of the first moment—the expectation—this merely reflects the linearity of a Lebesgue integral and has nothing to do with independence. For the variance, however, we have

$$\begin{aligned}
\operatorname{var}(X + Y) &= E(\{X - E(X) + Y - E(Y)\}^2) \\
&= E(\{X - E(X)\}^2) + 2E(\{X - E(X)\}\{Y - E(Y)\}) \\
&\quad + E(\{Y - E(Y)\}^2) = \operatorname{var}(X) + 0 + \operatorname{var}(Y),
\end{aligned}$$

where the vanishing of the cross product term is a consequence of Theorem 3.1 and uses independence.

We will also need "Chebyshev's inequality." Let X be any random variable, and f an increasing, nonnegative function on its range. Then

$$P(X \geq a) \leq \frac{E(f(X))}{f(a)} \tag{4}$$

provided $f(a) > 0$. The proof is very simple. From the discussion in Section 2 (in particular Problem 2.1) we can write

$$E(f(X)) = \int_{-\infty}^{\infty} f(x) \, dP_X.$$

[2] Transliterated Tchebycheff in [Ko]; several other versions are also in existence.

But since f is nonnegative and increasing

$$\int_{-\infty}^{\infty} f \, dP_X \geq \int_a^{\infty} f \, dP_X \geq f(a) \int_a^{\infty} dP_X = f(a)P(X \geq a),$$

which proves (4). The special case most often encountered is

$$P(|X - E(X)| \geq a) \leq \frac{\text{var } (X)}{a^2}, \qquad a > 0, \qquad (5)$$

obtained by choosing $f(x) = x^2$ and applying (4) to the random variable $|X - E(X)|$. Other cases we will encounter below are

$$P(X \geq a) \leq e^{-ca}E(e^{cX}), \qquad c > 0; \qquad (6)$$

$$P(|X| \geq a) \leq \frac{E(|X|^k)}{a^k}, \qquad a, k > 0. \qquad (7)$$

Problem 2. Show that the bound (5) is sharp in the sense that if a and σ^2 are given there is a random variable X for which equality occurs. When is the corresponding assertion true of (4)?

A "law of large numbers" of considerable generality can be proved very simply using these ideas:

Theorem 1. *For each n, let $X_1, \ldots, X_n$ be independent random variables, each having the same distribution function with finite second moment. Then for each $\epsilon > 0$*

$$\lim_{n \to \infty} P\left(\left|\frac{X_1 + \cdots + X_n}{n} - E(X_1)\right| \geq \epsilon\right) = 0. \qquad (8)$$

Proof. The random variables X_i have the same means and variances, say μ and σ^2; the mean and variance of $X_1 + \cdots + X_n = S_n$ are equal to $n\mu$ and $n\sigma^2$ respectively by additivity. Applying (5) to S_n with $a = n\epsilon$ therefore yields

$$P(|X_1 + \cdots + X_n - n\mu| \geq n\epsilon) \leq \frac{n\sigma^2}{(n\epsilon)^2}, \qquad (9)$$

and (8) follows immediately.

Remark. When setting down the foundations of probability it is perhaps plausible to introduce the concept of "expectation," but it is certainly not clear *a priori* that it has any intrinsic meaning for the theory. Theorem 1 shows that the appearance of this quantity is really inevitable—it is not

merely a technical device, however useful, but an essential idea
of the subject.

Example.   For Bernoulli trials, $\mu = p$ and $\sigma^2 = pq$ so that the estimate (9) becomes

$$P\left(\left| \frac{X_1 + \cdots + X_n}{n} - p \right| \geq \epsilon \right) \leq \frac{pq}{n\epsilon^2} \leq \frac{1}{4n\epsilon^2}. \qquad (10)$$

Far sharper bounds can be obtained for this special case, however.

Problem 3.   Using essentially the same methods, generalize the
statement and proof of Theorem 1 to s-dimensional random vectors.

The proof of Theorem 1 is actually capable of yielding much
more general results even in one dimension.   The distributions
of the random variables enter only through their means and
variances; let us call these μ_i and $\sigma_i{}^2$ respectively and not
assume they are identical.   Independence is only used via the
additivity of the variances, which in turn depended on the
property that

$$E[(X_i - \mu_i)(X_j - \mu_j)] = 0 \qquad \text{for all } i \neq j. \qquad (11)$$

Random variables satisfying (11) are called *uncorrelated*, and
need not be independent.   Exactly the same approach used
for Theorem 1 also proves a more general result:

Theorem 2.   *For each* n, *let* $X_1, \ldots, X_n$ *be uncorrelated
random variables, and assume that*

$$\lim_{n \to \infty} \frac{\displaystyle\sum_{i=1}^{n} \sigma_i{}^2}{n^2} = 0. \qquad (12)$$

Then for each $\epsilon > 0$,

$$\lim_{n \to \infty} P\left(\left| \frac{X_1 + \cdots + X_n}{n} - \frac{\mu_1 + \cdots + \mu_n}{n} \right| \geq \epsilon \right) = 0. \qquad (13)$$

One type of further generalization—weakening the hypothesis that the random variables are uncorrelated—is indicated in

Problems 5 and 6, which can also be solved by the methods introduced above. A little more terminology: the left side of (11) is called the *covariance* of X_i and X_j, and when the covariance is divided by the product of the standard deviations it becomes the *correlation coefficient*.

Problem 4. Show that the correlation coefficient of any two random variables lies between ± 1, that it is 0 if they are independent, and $+1$ or -1 if and only if they are linearly dependent.

Problem 5. Prove that if the covariance of X_i and X_j is nonpositive for $i \neq j$ and (12) holds, then so does (13).

Problem 6. (From [Ko], p. 62, corrected.) Suppose that the correlation coefficient of X_i and X_j is at most $c(|j - i|)$, and that $c(k) \geq 0$. Show that if $[c(0) + \cdots + c(n - 1)][\sigma_1{}^2 + \cdots + \sigma_n{}^2] = o(n^2)$ as $n \to \infty$ (13) is still true.

Another direction in which Theorem 1 can be generalized is to relax the assumption that m_2 be finite, while keeping the random variables independent and identically distributed. If the first moment still exists, not only the "weak law" (8) but more—the "strong law"—is true, as we shall see shortly. Moreover, a form of (8) is occasionally true even without the existence of $E(X)$; see [Ko], Chapter VI, Section 4. It is, of course, also possible to try and generalize in both ways simultaneously. We shall not pursue these matters further, but merely remark that in the independent case the problem has been completely solved, and refer to [GK].

A final comment. As was pointed out earlier about the Bernoulli set-up, it is not essential that all the random variables $X_1, X_2, \ldots$ be defined on a single probability space. If they are, however, we can restate our results in different terms. The conclusion (8) of Theorem 1, for instance, is equivalent to saying that the functions $(X_1 + \cdots + X_n)/n$ converge in probability to the constant μ. In the proof, we actually first demonstrated convergence in the mean (of order 2), and Chebyshev's inequality figured only in confirming that convergence in mean implies convergence in measure. These comments are true of Theorem 2 also. In Section 7 we shall turn to "strong laws," in which the convergence will be strengthened to the almost everywhere variety.

6. THE WEIERSTRASS APPROXIMATION THEOREM

This section is a short digression; we will show how the weak law of large numbers in the special case of Bernoulli trials leads to an elegant method of approximating a continuous function by polynomials. Let $f(x)$ be any bounded function on $[0, 1]$, and let $X_1, \ldots, X_n$ be independent with values 1 (probability $= p$) and 0 (probability $= 1 - p$) only. Then using (5.2) we have

$$E\left(f\left(\frac{X_1 + \cdots + X_n}{n}\right)\right) = \sum_{k=0}^{n} f\left(\frac{k}{n}\right)\binom{n}{k} p^k(1 - p)^{n-k}$$

$$= B_n(p). \quad (1)$$

The right-hand side is called a *Bernstein polynomial* after the discoverer of this proof of Weierstrass' theorem; it is clearly a polynomial in p with degree at most n. When n is large, most of the weight of the binomial distribution is concentrated on values of k such that k/n is nearly p; using this idea, we will prove the following theorem.

Theorem 1. *If f is continuous on the closed interval $[0, 1]$, then*

$$\lim_{n \to \infty} \max_{0 \le p \le 1} |f(p) - B_n(p)| = 0. \quad (2)$$

Proof. As with any continuous function on a compact space, f is bounded in absolute value (by M, say) and uniformly continuous. For any $\eta > 0$, choose ϵ so that

$$|f(x) - f(y)| \le \eta \quad \text{when } |x - y| \le \epsilon, \quad 0 \le x, y \le 1. \quad (3)$$

Then for any value of p we can write

$$|f(p) - B_n(p)| = \left| \sum_{k=0}^{n} \left[f(p) - f\left(\frac{k}{n}\right) \right] \binom{n}{k} p^k(1 - p)^{n-k} \right|$$

$$\le \sum_{\left|\frac{k}{n} - p\right| \le \epsilon} + \sum_{\left|\frac{k}{n} - p\right| > \epsilon} \left| f(p) - f\left(\frac{k}{n}\right) \right| \binom{n}{k} p^k(1 - p)^{n-k}.$$

The first sum is at most η by (3). The second is less than

$$2M \sum_{\left|\frac{k}{n} - p\right| > \epsilon} \binom{n}{k} p^k (1 - p)^{n-k}$$

$$= 2MP\left(\left|\frac{X_1 + \cdots + X_n}{n} - p\right| > \epsilon\right),$$

and the weak law of large numbers in the form (5.10) yields the upper bound $M(2n\epsilon^2)^{-1}$. Combining these things gives the estimate

$$\left|f(p) - B_n(p)\right| \leq \eta + \frac{M}{2n\epsilon^2}, \tag{4}$$

so that for large n the maximum error will be less than 2η, say. This completes the proof.

Problem 1. Prove the Weierstrass approximation theorem for a continuous function over the s-dimensional "unit cube," using the multinominal distribution (see [F]) and Problem 5.3.

7. THE STRONG LAW OF LARGE NUMBERS

Let us consider a situation almost the same as the set-up for Theorem 5.1: $X_1, X_2, \ldots$ are again independent random variables with the same distribution, which has at least a first moment. The major change will be that we now insist that all the X_i are defined simultaneously on some fixed probability space $(\Omega, \mathcal{B}, P)$. Then the conclusion—that the average of $X_1, \ldots, X_n$ tends to $\mu = E(X_i)$ as n increases—holds not only in measure but pointwise for each $\omega \in \Omega - A$, where A is a $\mathcal{B}$ set with $P(A) = 0$. This result, for the special case of Bernoulli trials, was formulated and proved by E. Borel in a famous paper [1] published in 1909 where the (then) new idea of Lebesgue integration was first applied to probability.

A great variety of theorems having to do with something which happens "almost surely" are attacked by means of the following lemma.

Borel-Cantelli Lemma. *Let $A_1, A_2, \ldots$ be events in a probability space, and let*

$$B = \limsup_{n \to \infty} A_n = \bigcap_{k=1}^{\infty} \bigcup_{n=k}^{\infty} A_n. \tag{1}$$

Then (i) if $\Sigma P(A_n) < \infty$, $P(B) = 0$, while (ii) if the events A_n are independent and $\Sigma P(A_n) = \infty$, then $P(B) = 1$.

Proof. All measures are subadditive with respect to (not necessarily disjoint) countable unions, so that

$$P(B) \le P(\bigcup_{n \ge k} A_n) \le \sum_{n \ge k} P(A_n)$$

for each k. If $\Sigma P(A_n) < \infty$, the right-hand side tends to 0 when k is chosen large; this proves (i).

For the partial converse, it is enough to show that

$$P(\bigcup_{n \ge k} A_n) = 1 \qquad (2)$$

for each k since the intersection of a sequence of sets, each with probability one, must also have probability one. But for each $K \ge k$

$$1 - P(\bigcup_{n \ge k} A_n) \le 1 - P(\bigcup_{n=k}^{K} A_n) = P(\bigcap_{n=k}^{K} [\Omega - A_n])$$

$$= \prod_{n=k}^{K} [1 - P(A_n)]$$

because the events A_n, and so also $\Omega - A_n$, are independent. If $\Sigma P(A_n) = \infty$, the product above diverges to 0 as $K \to \infty$ and (2) follows.

Remarks. B is the set of all ω which belong to infinitely many of the A_n; we interpret $P(B) = 0$ as "only finitely many A_n occur (a.s.)," etc. Applications of part (ii) of the lemma are greatly hampered by the requirement of independence, and a number of more general sufficient conditions have been discovered. But the condition cannot be dropped altogether—consider, for an extreme example, the case when all A_n are the same set, whose probability is neither 0 nor 1.

We can now prove quite simply one version of a strong law of large numbers:

Theorem 1. Let $X_1, X_2, \ldots$ be independent random variables having a common distribution with mean μ and finite fourth moment. Then

$$P\left(\lim_{n \to \infty} \frac{X_1 + \cdots + X_n}{n} = \mu\right) = 1. \qquad (3)$$

Proof. By expanding the fourth power and using Theorem 3.1, together with its extension in Problem 3.4, it is not difficult to calculate that

$$E\left(\left[\sum_{i=1}^{n}(X_i - \mu)\right]^4\right) = nE([X_1 - \mu]^4) + 6\binom{n}{2}\sigma^4 \le Cn^2. \quad (4)$$

(Here $\sigma^2 = E((X_i - \mu)^2)$ is finite by Problem 5.1.) But applying the Chebyshev inequality in the form (5.7) yields

$$P\left(\left|\sum_{i=1}^{n}(X_i - \mu)\right| > \epsilon n\right) \le \frac{Cn^2}{(\epsilon n)^4}, \quad (5)$$

and the sum on n of the right-hand side is finite. From the Borel-Cantelli lemma we therefore can conclude that with probability one, only finitely many of the events

$$A_n^{(\epsilon)} = \left\{\omega: \left|\frac{X_1 + \cdots + X_n}{n} - \mu\right| > \epsilon\right\}$$

occur; that is, $P(B_\epsilon) = 0$, where $B_\epsilon = \limsup A_n^{(\epsilon)}$. The sets B_ϵ increase as $\epsilon \searrow 0$ to the ω set on which $(X_1 + \cdots + X_n)/n \nrightarrow \mu$. Thus, letting $\epsilon \searrow 0$ through a countable set of values such as k^{-1}, we have

$$P\left(\left\{\omega: \frac{X_1 + \cdots + X_n}{n} - \mu \nrightarrow 0\right\}\right) = P(\cup_k B_{k^{-1}}) = 0,$$

which proves Theorem 1. (The last step will often be taken for granted in future proofs of this sort.)

There is an interesting nonprobabilistic application of the strong law, also due to Borel. A number $x \in [0, 1]$ is *normal to base d* if each digit occurs the "right" fraction of the time (namely, $1/d$) when x is expanded in the number system based on d; x is *normal* if it is normal to base d for every $d > 1$. Rational numbers are never normal, although they may be normal to a particular base. (For example, $1/3 = 0.010101$ . . . in binary notation and so is normal to base 2.)

Theorem 2. *Almost all* [3] *numbers are normal.*

[3] That is, all except for a set of Lebesgue measure 0.

Proof. Take the unit interval with Lebesgue measure as a probability space, and consider the binary expansion $x = .b_1 b_2 b_3 \ldots$, $b_i = 0$ or 1, with any convention adopted to make the expansion unique. Then the digits $b_i(x)$ are random variables on the space. It is not difficult to see that they are independent and that each takes the values 0 and 1 with equal probability $1/2$. By the strong law of large numbers, then, we have

$$P\left(\left\{x : \frac{b_1(x) + \cdots + b_n(x)}{n} \to \frac{1}{2}\right\}\right) = 1$$

so that almost all x are normal to base 2. Pretty nearly the same proof applies using any other base, and since the set of x which are not normal is the union of the exceptional sets for each base—each of measure 0—the theorem follows. Incidentally, although a "random" number is a.s. normal, it is not so obvious how to exhibit a number for which normality can be proved!

Problem 1. Verify that $b_i(x)$ are independent and that $P(b_i(x) = 1) = 1/2$.

Problem 2. Give the proof for a.s. normality to base d, $d > 2$.

Problem 3. Let $X_1, X_2, \ldots$ represent general independent Bernoulli trials; that is, $P(X_i = 1) = p$, $P(X_i = 0) = 1 - p$. Let

$$Z = \sum_{n=1}^{\infty} X_n 2^{-n}, \qquad F_p(x) = P(Z \leq x). \qquad (6)$$

Prove, for $0 \leq x \leq 1$, that $F_{1/2}(x) = x$ and that if $0 < p < 1$ and $p \neq 1/2$ then F_p is a continuous, strictly increasing singular distribution. (That is, $F'_p(x) = 0$ for almost (Lebesgue) all x).

8. THE STRONG LAW—CONTINUED

There are many generalizations of the theorem we have proved, but we will focus on establishing a complete result in the identically distributed case.

Theorem 1. *Let $X_1, X_2, \ldots$ be independent random variables with the same distribution, which has a mean μ. Then*

$$P\left(\lim_{n \to \infty} \frac{X_1 + \cdots + X_n}{n} = \mu\right) = 1. \qquad (1)$$

Conversely, if the expectation of X_i does not exist, then

$$P \left(\limsup_{n \to \infty} \left| \frac{X_1 + \cdots + X_n}{n} \right| = + \infty \right) = 1. \qquad (2)$$

The proof will require several preliminaries, which are of interest in their own right. The first of these is the following:

Kolmogorov's Inequality. *Let $X_1, \ldots, X_n$ be independent random variables with mean 0 and variances σ_i^2. Then for any $a > 0$,*

$$P(\max_{i \leq n} |X_1 + \cdots + X_i| \geq a) \leq \frac{\sum_{i=1}^{n} \sigma_i^2}{a^2}. \qquad (3)$$

Proof. Let us write $S_i = X_1 + \cdots + X_i$ and define the events

$$A = \{\omega : \max_{i \leq n} |S_i| \geq a\};$$
$$A_j = \{\omega : |S_i| < a \text{ for } i < j, |S_j| \geq a\}. \qquad (4)$$

Then clearly the A_j are disjoint and $\bigcup_{j=1}^{n} A_j = A$. Now, since the random variables have 0 mean,

$$\sum_{i=1}^{n} \sigma_i^2 = E(S_n^2) \geq E(S_n^2 \phi_A) = \sum_{j=1}^{n} E(S_n^2 \phi_{A_j}).$$

($\phi_A(\omega)$ is again the "indicator function" of A: 1 if $\omega \in A$, 0 otherwise.) But

$$E(S_n^2 \phi_{A_j}) = E([S_j + (S_n - S_j)]^2 \phi_{A_j})$$
$$= E(S_j^2 \phi_{A_j}) + 2E(S_j(S_n - S_j)\phi_{A_j})$$
$$+ E(\phi_{A_j}(S_n - S_j)^2).$$

The second of these terms vanishes, for $(S_n - S_j)$ and $S_j \phi_{A_j}$ are independent since they are functions of $(X_{j+1}, \ldots, X_n)$ and $(X_1, \ldots, X_j)$ respectively,[4] and we can use Theorem 3.1.

[4] This statement, although perhaps "intuitively obvious," really requires a proof. Matters of the sort are discussed in detail in Section 10, and we defer this point until then. (Section 10, of course, does not depend on the other material in this chapter and can, if desired, be read right away.)

Also, the last term is nonnegative, and when $\omega \in A_j$ we have $S_j{}^2 \geq a^2$ by definition. Putting these things together yields

$$E(S_n{}^2 \phi_{A_j}) \geq a^2 P(A_j)$$

and hence

$$\sum_{i=1}^{n} \sigma_i{}^2 \geq a^2 \sum_{j=1}^{n} P(A_j) = a^2 P(A),$$

which is the same as (3).

Remark. It is interesting to compare Kolmogorov's inequality with Chebyshev's in the form (5.5); if $n = 1$ they are the same.

The next result, although a lemma for the proof of Theorem 1 and a corollary of Kolmogorov's inequality, still deserves a title of its own.

Theorem 2. *Let* $X_1, X_2, \ldots$ *be independent random variables with means 0 and variances* $\sigma_i{}^2$ *and suppose that* $\sum_{i=1}^{\infty} \sigma_i{}^2 < \infty$. *Then*

$$P\left(\sum_{i=1}^{\infty} X_i \text{ converges} \right) = 1. \qquad (5)$$

Proof. By (3),

$$P(\max_{i \leq n} |S_{N+i} - S_N| > \epsilon) \leq \frac{\sum_{i=N+1}^{N+n} \sigma_i{}^2}{\epsilon^2}.$$

If we let $n \to \infty$ and then $N \to \infty$, this implies that

$$P(|S_j - S_i| > 2\epsilon \text{ for arbitrarily large } i \text{ and } j) = 0. \qquad (6)$$

Taking a sequence of $\epsilon_k \searrow 0$, since (6) must hold simultaneously for each of them we see that the partial sums $\{S_j\}$ form a Cauchy sequence with probability 1.

Remark. The assumptions state in part that we are dealing with a series of perpendicular vectors in the Hilbert space $L_2(\Omega)$ which converges in the norm (since $\Sigma \sigma_i{}^2 < \infty$); this interpretation uses only "orthogonality" and not the independence of the X_i. Such a series of functions, of course, does not need to converge almost everywhere—that is where independence makes the difference.

To complete the proof of Theorem 1, we need three lemmas which are themselves not of a probabilistic nature.

Lemma 1. *If $\{a_n\}$ is a sequence of numbers such that $\Sigma(a_n/n)$ converges, then $(a_1 + \cdots + a_n)/n \to 0$.*

Lemma 2. *Let F be a probability distribution function. Then*

$$\int_0^\infty x \, dF(x) = \int_0^\infty (1 - F(x)) \, dx \qquad \text{and}$$

$$\int_{-\infty}^0 x \, dF(x) = -\int_{-\infty}^0 F(x) \, dx, \quad (7)$$

where in both cases the two sides exist or diverge together.

We leave the proofs as **Problem** 1 and **Problem** 2, respectively. Combining Lemma 1 with Theorem 2 yields the following strong law of large numbers, which is much more general than Theorem 7.1:

Theorem 3. *Let $X_1, X_2, \ldots$ be independent random variables with means μ_i and variances $\sigma_i{}^2$. If $\displaystyle\sum_{i=1}^\infty \sigma_i{}^2/i^2 < \infty$, then*

$$P\left(\lim_{n\to\infty}\left[\frac{X_1 + \cdots + X_n}{n} - \frac{\mu_1 + \cdots + \mu_n}{n}\right] = 0\right) = 1. \quad (8)$$

Proof. The random variables $(X_i - \mu_i)/i$ have means 0 and variances $\sigma_i{}^2/i^2$, so that Theorem 2 applies to them and yields

$$P\left(\sum_{i=1}^\infty \frac{X_i - \mu_i}{i} \text{ converges}\right) = 1.$$

Transforming this conclusion by Lemma 1 above, we obtain (8).

Lemma 3. *If F is a distribution function such that*

$$\int_{-\infty}^\infty |x| \, dF(x) < \infty,$$

then

$$\sum_{n=1}^{\infty} \frac{1}{n^2} \int_{-n}^{n} x^2 \, dF(x) < \infty. \tag{9}$$

Proof. Let

$$a_{n+1} = \int_{n}^{n+1} x \, dF(x) + \int_{-(n+1)}^{-n} |x| \, dF(x);$$

then

$$a_n \geq 0 \quad \text{and} \quad \sum_{n=1}^{\infty} a_n = \int_{-\infty}^{\infty} |x| \, dF(x) < \infty.$$

But it is easy to see that

$$\int_{-(n+1)}^{-n} x^2 \, dF + \int_{n}^{n+1} x^2 \, dF \leq (n+1)a_{n+1},$$

and so

$$\sum_{n=1}^{\infty} \frac{1}{n^2} \int_{-n}^{n} x^2 \, dF(x) \leq \sum_{n=1}^{\infty} \frac{1}{n^2} \sum_{l=1}^{n} l a_l = \sum_{l=1}^{\infty} l a_l \sum_{n=l}^{\infty} \frac{1}{n^2}.$$

The sum on n in the last expression is, for large l, asymptotic to $\int_{l}^{\infty} (dx/x^2) = 1/l$, and so the terms of the summation on l behave like a_l. Since $\Sigma a_l < \infty$, (9) follows.

At last we are ready to prove Theorem 1. First we assume that the X_i have mean 0, for if not we simply work with the variables $X_i - \mu$ instead. Since all of the techniques developed so far depend on variances or higher moments, these must be made to exist by the "method of truncation." Define

$$Y_i = \begin{cases} X_i & \text{if } |X_i| \leq i, \\ 0 & \text{if } |X_i| > i, \end{cases} \tag{10}$$

and write $X_i = Y_i + Z_i$ for each i. The idea of the proof will be to show that all but finitely many of the Z_i are 0, so they do not count in the limit, while methods based on moments can be applied to the Y_i.

First, we will dispose of the Z_i. Note that

$$P(Z_n \neq 0) = P(|X_n| > n) \leq 1 - F(n) + F(-n),$$

where F is the common distribution function of the X_i.[5]   But

$$\sum_{n=1}^{\infty} P(Z_n \neq 0) \leq \sum_{n=1}^{\infty} \{1 - F(n) + F(-n)\}$$

$$\leq \int_0^{\infty} (1 - F(x))\, dx + \int_{-\infty}^0 F(x)\, dx$$

$$= \int_{-\infty}^{\infty} |x|\, dF(x) = E(|X_i|) < \infty,$$

using Lemma 2 and the assumption that the mean exists. Thus, by the Borel-Cantelli lemma,

$$P(Z_n \neq 0 \text{ for infinitely many } n) = 0. \tag{11}$$

We will next apply Theorem 3 to the Y's.   Because of the truncation $\mu_n = E(Y_n)$ need not be 0, but in any case

$$\text{var } (Y_n) \leq E(Y_n{}^2) = \int_{-n}^n x^2\, dF(x),$$

and so by Lemma 3

$$\sum_{n=1}^{\infty} \frac{\text{var } (Y_n)}{n^2} < \infty.$$

We conclude that (8) holds for $\{Y_i\}$.   But

$$E(Y_n) = \int_{-n}^n x\, dF(x)$$

so that $\mu_n \to \int_{-\infty}^{\infty} x\, dF = 0$ as $n \to \infty$.   Combining this, (8), and (11), it is clear that

$$P\left(\frac{S_n}{n} \to 0\right) = P\left(\frac{Y_1 + \cdots + Y_n}{n} + \frac{Z_1 + \cdots + Z_n}{n} \to 0\right) = 1,$$

which is the same as (1) and proves the main part of the theorem.

For the converse, assume $E(|X_i|) = +\infty$.   Then for any constant C, we define the events

$$A_n = \{\omega \colon |X_n(\omega)| \geq Cn\}.$$

[5] Inequality only occurs when there is positive probability that $X_n = -n$.

Using Lemma 2 it is easy to see that $\Sigma P(A_n) = \infty$; the A_n are independent since the X_n are. By the second part of the B.-C. lemma, therefore,

$$P(|X_n| > Cn \text{ for arbitrarily large } n) = 1$$

for each C. It is not difficult to deduce (2), and the proof is then complete.

Problem 3. Supply details for the last step above.

9. CONVERGENCE OF SERIES

Since we have already done some work on the convergence of series of independent random variables while investigating the law of large numbers, it seems worthwhile to go a bit further and discuss Kolmogorov's necessary and sufficient condition. We define the *truncation at c* of the random variable X by

$$X^{(c)} = \begin{cases} X & \text{if } |X| \le c, \\ 0 & \text{if } |X| > c. \end{cases} \tag{1}$$

Three Series Theorem. *Let* $X_1, X_2, \ldots$ *be independent r.v.'s. Then*

$$P\left(\sum_{n=1}^{\infty} X_n \text{ exists}\right) = 1 \tag{2}$$

if and only if, for some c, *each of the following series converges:*

$$\sum_{n=1}^{\infty} P(|X_n| > c); \qquad \sum_{n=1}^{\infty} E(X_n^{(c)}); \qquad \sum_{n=1}^{\infty} \text{var}(X_n^{(c)}). \tag{3}$$

Proof. Let us first assume the convergence of the three series. The convergence of the first one, with the B.-C. lemma, implies that $X_n = X_n^{(c)}$ for all but finitely many n (a.s.), so the problem is reduced to showing convergence of $\Sigma X_n^{(c)}$. Because the variances converge, we have by Theorem 8.2 that

$$P\left(\sum_{n=1}^{\infty} [X_n^{(c)} - E(X_n^{(c)})] \text{ converges}\right) = 1,$$

and since $\Sigma E(X_n^{(c)})$ converges too we can conclude that $\Sigma X_n^{(c)}$ converges a.s.

The converse takes a little longer, since we have not made the necessary preparations in advance. Assume (2). Then $X_n \to 0$ a.s. so that $X_n = X_n^{(c)}$ for all large n (any $c > 0$); by B.-C. lemma, part (ii), the first of the three series in (3) has finite sum. To handle the other two, we need several lemmas.

Lemma 1. *Let $X_1, \ldots, X_n$ be independent r.v.'s with means 0 and variances σ_i^2, and assume that $|X_i| \leq c$ a.s. for each $i \leq n$. Then for each $a > 0$,*

$$P(\max_{i \leq n} |S_i| > a) \geq 1 - \frac{(a + c)^2}{\displaystyle\sum_{i=1}^{n} \sigma_i^2}. \tag{4}$$

Proof. The approach is similar to that for Kolmogorov's inequality, and in particular we will use sets A, A_j defined just as in (8.4) except that "$\geq a$" is replaced by "$> a$" and "$< a$" by "$\leq a$". Proceeding as before,

$$
\begin{aligned}
E(S_n{}^2\phi_A) &= \sum_{j=1}^{n} E(S_n{}^2\phi_{A_j}) = \sum_{j=1}^{n} E([S_j + (S_n - S_j)]^2\phi_{A_j}) \\
&= \sum_{j=1}^{n} E(S_j{}^2\phi_{A_j}) + 0 + \sum_{j=1}^{n} E([S_n - S_j]^2\phi_{A_j}).
\end{aligned}
$$

This time we need an upper bound. In the set A_j, $|S_{j-1}| \leq a$ and so $|S_j| \leq a + c$. Also, ϕ_{A_j} and $(S_n - S_j)$ are independent since they are respectively functions of $X_1, \ldots, X_j$ and $X_{j+1}, \ldots, X_n$ (see the footnote to the proof of Kolmogorov's inequality). Hence we can write

$$
\begin{aligned}
E(S_n{}^2\phi_A) &\leq (a + c)^2 \sum_{j=1}^{n} P(A_j) + \sum_{j=1}^{n} P(A_j) \sum_{l=j+1}^{n} \sigma_l^2 \\
&\leq \left[(a + c)^2 + \sum_{l=1}^{n} \sigma_l^2 \right] P(A).
\end{aligned}
$$

On the other hand,

$$E(S_n{}^2\phi_A) = E(S_n{}^2) - E(S_n{}^2\phi_{\Omega-A}) \geq \sum_{i=1}^{n} \sigma_i^2 - a^2 P(\Omega - A)$$

since $|S_n| \leq a$ in the complement of A. Combining these inequalities and solving for $P(A)$ we obtain

$$P(A) \geq \frac{\sum_{l=1}^{n} \sigma_l{}^2 - a^2}{(a+c)^2 - a^2 + \sum_{l=1}^{n} \sigma_l{}^2} = 1 - \frac{(a+c)^2}{(a+c)^2 - a^2 + \Sigma\sigma_l{}^2}$$

$$\geq 1 - \frac{(a+c)^2}{\Sigma\sigma_l{}^2}.$$

Lemma 2. *If $X_1, X_2, \ldots$ are independent with means 0 and variances $\sigma_i{}^2$, if $|X| \leq c$ a.s. for each i, and if ΣX_i converges a.s., then $\Sigma\sigma_i{}^2$ converges too.*

Proof. From the a.s. convergence of the series ΣX_i it follows that as $N \to \infty$ $\max_{i \geq N} |S_{N+i} - S_N| \to 0$ a.s.; hence there is also convergence in probability and so for $a > 0$

$$\lim_{N \to \infty} P(\max_{i \geq 0} |S_{N+i} - S_N| > a) = 0.$$

Fix an N for which this probability is $\leq 1/2$, say. But by Lemma 1,

$$P(\max_{0 \leq i \leq n} |S_{N+i} - S_N| > a) \geq 1 - \frac{(a+c)^2}{\displaystyle\sum_{i=N}^{N+n} \sigma_i{}^2},$$

and if the sum of the variances does not converge the left-hand side must tend to 1 as $n \to \infty$, a contradiction.

The plan, of course, is to apply Lemma 2 to the $X_n^{(c)}$ of the three series theorem. This cannot be done directly, however, since $X_n^{(c)}$ will not in general have mean 0. To avoid this difficulty, we introduce a new sequence of random variables $\{Y_n\}$, independent of each other and of the X_n's, such that for each n, Y_n and $X_n^{(c)}$ have the same distribution.[6] Consider the series $\Sigma(X_n^{(c)} - Y_n)$. It converges a.s. since $\Sigma X_n^{(c)}$ and ΣY_n

---

[6] This may not be possible on the original probability space where the variables $\{X_n\}$ are defined, but both sequences can be defined at once on *some* space, and that is good enough. For example, the direct product of the original space with itself will always do.

(having the same distribution) do; we have $|X_n^{(c)} - Y_n| \le 2c$ a.s. and $E(X_n^{(c)} - Y_n) = 0$. The terms are independent, and var $(X_n^{(c)} - Y_n) = 2$ var $(X_n^{(c)})$. From Lemma 2, then, we conclude that the third series in (3) is finite. Looking back to Theorem 8.2 we also obtain the a.s. convergence of $\Sigma[X_n^{(c)} - E(X_n^{(c)})]$, and since $\Sigma X_n^{(c)}$ converges a.s. the convergence of $\Sigma E(X_n^{(c)})$ is clear and the theorem is proved.

Remarks. As the proof shows, the convergence of the random series implies that for every $c > 0$ the three series of (3) converge also. We will see in the next section that if ΣX_i does not converge a.s. it has to diverge a.s.; it is an all or nothing situation.

For random series which converge a.s., the probability of absolute convergence must be either 0 or 1 by the remark above (applied to $\Sigma|X_n|$). But there is an intermediate concept: the series may have the property, implied by a.s. absolute convergence, that it is still a.s. convergent no matter in what order the random variables are arranged. This possibility is illustrated by the following example.

Example. Let $\{Y_n\}$ be independent random variables such that $Y_n = \pm n^{-1}$, each with probability 1/2, and let μ_n be constants tending to 0. Define $X_n = Y_n + \mu_n$, and consider the random series ΣX_n. It is easy to see that the probability of absolute convergence is 0. Looking at the condition (3) of the three series theorem, we see that the first and third series must always be finite, so ΣX_n exists a.s. if and only if the series $\Sigma \mu_n$ converges. If the latter converges absolutely, then ΣX_n is a.s. convergent no matter how the terms are reordered, but if $\Sigma \mu_n$ is conditionally convergent, a permutation which destroys its convergence does the same for the a.s. convergence of ΣX_n. It is possible to give general criteria for these stronger modes of convergence, and for convergence of $\Sigma(X_n - a_n)$ for some sequence of "centering constants" $\{a_n\}$, but we will not pursue the subject further. (See [Do] or [Lo].)

10. MORE ON INDEPENDENCE; THE 0-1 LAW

Kolmogorov's 0-1 law states roughly that if $X_1, X_2, \ldots$ is a sequence of independent r.v.'s and if A is an event defined in terms of the X_n's whose occurrence is unchanged by altering any finite number of them, then $P(A) = 0$ or $P(A) = 1$. For example, a sequence or a series of independent r.v.'s must either converge a.s. or diverge a.s.; there is no middle ground. The proof of the 0-1 law itself is very short, but we must first make some preparations which will serve also to clarify certain points about independence that have been treated rather cavalierly above.

Any set $\mathfrak{X}$ of random variables on a probability space $(\Omega, \mathfrak{B}, P)$ determines a Borel field $\mathfrak{B}(\mathfrak{X})$ defined as the smallest subfield of $\mathfrak{B}$ with respect to which each r.v. $X \in \mathfrak{X}$ is measurable. In fact, $\mathfrak{B}(\mathfrak{X})$ is the intersection of all Borel subfields of $\mathfrak{B}$ which contain every set of the form $\{\omega : X(\omega) \in S\}$, where $X \in \mathfrak{X}$ and S is a Borel set in $\mathfrak{R}^1$. If $X_1, X_2, \ldots$ are independent random variables, and if $A_i \in \mathfrak{B}(X_i)$,[7] then by the definition of independence we have for each n

$$P(A_1 \cap \cdots \cap A_n) = \prod_{i=1}^{n} P(A_i). \qquad (1)$$

It is convenient to generalize this a bit: if $\mathfrak{B}_1, \mathfrak{B}_2, \ldots$ is a sequence of Borel fields (subfields of $\mathfrak{B}$) such that (1) holds whenever $A_i \in \mathfrak{B}_i$, we shall say that *the fields $\mathfrak{B}_i$ are independent*. We need the following:

Theorem 1. *Let $\mathfrak{B}_0, \mathfrak{B}_1, \mathfrak{B}_2, \ldots$ be independent Borel fields, in the sense defined above. If $\mathcal{G}$ is the Borel field generated by any subset (finite or not) of $\mathfrak{B}_1, \mathfrak{B}_2, \ldots$, then $\mathfrak{B}_0$ and $\mathcal{G}$ are independent.*

Proof. It is enough to consider the case where $\mathcal{G}$ is the smallest field containing the members of each $\mathfrak{B}_i$, $i \geq 1$. Let $A \in \mathfrak{B}_0$; we need to show that

$$P(A \cap G) = P(A)P(G) \qquad (2)$$

for all $G \in \mathcal{G}$. We will confine ourselves to the case $P(A) > 0$, as (2) is trivial otherwise. If G is of the form $A_1 \cap \cdots \cap A_n$, where $A_i \in \mathfrak{B}_i$, then (2) holds by definition. The class $\mathfrak{F}$ of finite unions of such sets forms a finitely additive field, and we next check that (2) holds if $G \in \mathfrak{F}$. Let $G_i = A_1^i \cap \cdots \cap A_{n_i}^i$, and let $G = \bigcup_{i=1}^{k} G_i$ be an arbitrary set in $\mathfrak{F}$. By using

---

[7] Strictly speaking this should be written $\mathfrak{B}(\{X_i\})$, meaning $\mathfrak{B}(\mathfrak{X})$ when $\mathfrak{X}$ is a one-element set, but we omit the braces. $\mathfrak{B}(X_i)$ consists exactly of the inverse images, under X_i, of the Borel sets on the real line.

the "inclusion-exclusion" formula for the probability of a finite union of sets (see [F], p. 89) we can write

$$P(A \cap G) = P(\bigcup_{i=1}^{k} (A \cap G_i)) \tag{3}$$

$$= \sum_{i} P(A \cap G_i) - \sum_{i<j} P(A \cap G_i \cap G_j)$$

$$+ \sum_{i<j<k} P(A \cap G_i \cap G_j \cap G_k) - \cdots ;$$

the series has k terms. But each set $G_i \cap G_j \cap G_k$, and so on, is of the form for which (2) is known to hold. Thus the factor $P(A)$ can be taken out of each term of the sum in (3) by deleting the set A from the intersection; the result is $P(A)$, multiplying a sum which (again by the inclusion-exclusion formula) equals $P(\bigcup_{i=1}^{k} G_i)$. Thus (2) holds for all $G \in \mathfrak{F}$.

The rest of the proof is very easy. Both P and P_A are probability measures on $\mathcal{B}$, where $P_A(B) = P(B \cap A)/P(A)$ is the conditional probability measure given A; the two, as we have seen, agree on $\mathfrak{F}$. By the uniqueness part of the basic extension theorem (Section 1) they must therefore agree at least on the Borel field generated by $\mathfrak{F}$, which is $\mathcal{G}$; this proves the theorem.

Problem 1. Show by an example that it is not enough to assume only that $\mathcal{B}_0$ and $\mathcal{B}_i$ are independent for each $i \geq 1$.

Corollary 1. *Under the conditions of the theorem, if $\mathcal{G}_1$ and $\mathcal{G}_2$ are the Borel fields generated by two disjoint subsets of the $\mathcal{B}_n$ then $\mathcal{G}_1$ and $\mathcal{G}_2$ are independent.*

Proof. Each $\mathcal{B}_i$ which helps to generate $\mathcal{G}_1$ is independent of $\mathcal{G}_2$ by the theorem. Taking $\mathcal{G}_2$, then, in the role of $\mathcal{B}_0$, another application of the theorem finishes the job.

Problem 2. Generalize Corollary 1 to the case of more than two disjoint subsets of the fields $\mathcal{B}_n$.

Corollary 2. *Let $X_1, \ldots, X_{n+m}$ be independent r.v.'s and let f and g be respectively real Borel functions on R^n and R^m. Then $f(X_1, \ldots, X_n)$ and $g(X_{n+1}, \ldots, X_{n+m})$ are independent r.v.'s.*

We will leave the proof of this fact to constitute **Problem 3.** This result justifies some of our earlier manipulations as, for instance, in the proof of Kolmogorov's inequality.

Corollary 3. *If* $X_1, \ldots, X_n$ *are independent r.v.'s with expectations, then*

$$E \left(\prod_{i=1}^{n} X_i \right) = \prod_{i=1}^{n} E(X_i). \tag{4}$$

Proof. (Recall Problem 3.4, and the remark following it.) By Corollary 2 above, we know that X_1 and $\prod_{i=2}^{n} X_i$ are independent. Hence if the latter has an expectation, we have

$$E \left(\prod_{i=1}^{n} X_i \right) = E(X_1) E \left(\prod_{i=2}^{n} X_i \right)$$

by Theorem 3.1. Equation (4) therefore follows by a straightforward induction on n.

There are versions of this result for infinite products, and we will need the following special one in Section 21 below.

Corollary 4. *Let* $X_1, X_2, \ldots$ *be independent (real valued) random variables such that* ΣX_n *exists a.s. Then*

$$E \left(\exp \left[i \sum_{n=1}^{\infty} X_n \right] \right) = \prod_{n=1}^{\infty} E(\exp iX_n). \tag{5}$$

Proof. There is no doubt that the expectation on the left exists, since the random variable has absolute value 1 everywhere. Moreover, by the Lebesgue bounded convergence theorem we have

$$E \left(\exp \left[i \sum_{n=1}^{\infty} X_n \right] \right) = \lim_{N \to \infty} E \left(\exp \left[i \sum_{n=1}^{N} X_n \right] \right)$$

$$= \lim_{N \to \infty} E \left(\prod_{n=1}^{N} \exp iX_n \right).$$

But using Corollary 3 (or Problem 3.4), the latter expression is seen to be just the right side of (5).

Now we are ready for the 0-1 law. If $\{X_n\}$ is a sequence of r.v.'s, the Borel fields $\mathcal{B}(\{X_n, X_{n+1}, \ldots\})$ are obviously decreasing as n increases and their intersection is called the *tail field* of the sequence.

Theorem 2 (*0-1 Law*). *Any set belonging to the tail field of a sequence of independent r.v.'s has probability either 0 or 1.*

Proof. Let $\mathcal{B}_\infty$ denote the tail field. By Theorem 1 we know that $\mathcal{B}(X_n)$ is independent of $\mathcal{B}(\{X_{n+1}, X_{n+2}, \ldots\}) \supset \mathcal{B}_\infty$, so $\mathcal{B}_\infty$ is independent of $\mathcal{B}(X_n)$ for every n. Again by Theorem 1, it follows that $\mathcal{B}_\infty$ is independent of $\mathcal{B}(\{X_1, X_2, \ldots\})$. But this last field *contains* $\mathcal{B}_\infty$, which must therefore be independent of itself! In particular, then, if $A \in \mathcal{B}_\infty$ we have

$$P(A) = P(A \cap A) = P(A)^2,$$

so that $P(A)$ must be 0 or 1.

Problem 4. Justify the assertions at the beginning of this section by verifying that for any sequence of r.v.'s the ω-sets on which $\lim X_n$ and ΣX_n exist both belong to the tail field of the sequence.

11. THE LAW OF THE ITERATED LOGARITHM

Throughout this section $X_1, X_2, \ldots$ will be independent r.v.'s with a common nondegenerate distribution having first moment zero. We saw in Theorem 8.1 that under these assumptions $|S_n| = o(n)$ a.s., and in general nothing stronger can be said along these lines. But if additional restrictions are put on the distribution of the X_i it is natural to hope for sharper bounds, and it is remarkable that very precise results can be obtained under quite general conditions.

If X_i takes the values -1 or 1 with probabilities $1/2$, then as we saw in connection with Theorem 7.2 the probability space can be taken as $[0, 1]$ with Lebesgue measure, and $X_n(x) = 2b_n(x) - 1$ where $b_n(x)$ is the n'th digit in the binary expansion of x. In this situation statements about S_n can be phrased in terms of the number of 1's among the first n binary digits of x, and that is the context in which the problem was first studied.   The early results were as follows:

1913. $|S_n| = O(n^{(1/2)+\epsilon})$ a.s. for any $\epsilon > 0$ (Hausdorff).
1914. $|S_n| = O(\sqrt{n \log n})$ a.s.   (Hardy and Littlewood).
1923. $|S_n| = O(\sqrt{n \log \log n})$ a.s.   (Khintchine).
1924.   The last bound is best possible, and moreover

$$\limsup_{n \to \infty} \frac{|S_n|}{\sqrt{n \log \log n}} = \sqrt{2} \text{ a.s.} \quad \text{(Khintchine).} \quad (1)$$

Then a few years later the last result was generalized by Kolmogorov to a wide class of sequences of independent r.v.'s.

We will develop these results in the historical order, which makes their proofs seem more natural than they might in isolation.   However, there is no gain in adhering to the Bernoulli case even temporarily.

Hausdorff's Estimate.   *If the common distribution of X_i has finite moments of all orders (≥ 0), then $|S_n| = O(n^{(1/2)+\epsilon})$ a.s. for any $\epsilon > 0$.*

Proof.   In our first approach to the strong law of large numbers (in Section 7) we established the fact that $E(S_n^4) \leq Cn^2$ for some constant C.   By Chebyshev's inequality (5.7) this implies that

$$P(|S_n| > an^\alpha) \leq \frac{Cn^2}{a^4 n^{4\alpha}}. \quad (2)$$

To insure that the inequality $|S_n| > an^\alpha$ occurs only finitely often (a.s.) it is therefore sufficient that the sum of the right-hand side of (2) be finite.   This is the case if $\alpha > 3/4$, so we have proved $|S_n| = O(n^{(3/4)+\epsilon})$ a.s. for any $\epsilon > 0$.

We can get sharper results by using higher moments.   It is not too hard to verify that

$$E(S_n^{2k}) \leq Cn^k, \qquad k = 1, 2, 3, \ldots, \quad (3)$$

where C depends on k but not on n.   Using (3), the bound in (2) can be replaced by $Cn^k/(an^\alpha)^{2k}$, and the B.-C. lemma yields $|S_n| = O(n^\alpha)$ a.s. provided $\alpha > (k+1)/2k$.   Since k can be chosen to make this as close to $1/2$ as desired, the stated conclusion follows.

Problem 1.   Prove (3).

There are two tricks involved in the two improvements of Hausdorff's estimate. Curiously enough, they can be introduced in any order: either one will suffice to improve the bound above to $O(\sqrt{n \log n})$, and then adding the other makes it $O(\sqrt{n \log \log n})$. Perhaps the most plausible approach, however, is to reflect at this point that we got better and better results above by considering $E(S_n^{2k})$ and letting k increase, and the "limit" to this process might be to use an exponential function in place of a power. To follow up this idea, we need an estimate to replace (3):

Lemma 1. *Suppose that* $|X_i| \leq M$ *a.s. Then for any* $0 \leq x \leq \dfrac{2}{M}$,

$$E(e^{xS_n}) \leq \exp\left[\frac{nx^2\sigma^2}{2}(1 + xM)\right]. \tag{4}$$

Proof. The random variables e^{xX_i} are independent, so that Theorem 3.1 (plus Problem 3.4 or Corollary 10.3) and the fact that the X_i have a common distribution imply that

$$E(e^{xS_n}) = E(e^{xX_1})^n. \tag{5}$$

But using the boundedness and zero mean of X_1, we get for any $x \geq 0$

$$E(e^{xX_1}) = E\left(\sum_{k=0}^{\infty} \frac{x^k X_1^k}{k!}\right)$$

$$= 1 + 0 + \frac{x^2\sigma^2}{2} + \sum_{k=3}^{\infty} \frac{x^k E(X_1^k)}{k!}$$

$$\leq 1 + \frac{\sigma^2 x^2}{2} + \sum_{k=3}^{\infty} \frac{x^k M^{k-2} E(X_1^2)}{k!}$$

$$\leq 1 + \frac{\sigma^2 x^2}{2} + \frac{\sigma^2}{3!} \sum_{k=3}^{\infty} \frac{x^k M^{k-2}}{3^{k-3}}$$

$$= 1 + \frac{\sigma^2 x^2}{2} + \frac{\sigma^2}{3!} \frac{x^3 M}{1 - (xM/3)}.$$

If we assume $x \leq 2/M$, the bound becomes

$$E(e^{xX_1}) \leq 1 + \frac{\sigma^2 x^2}{2}(1 + xM) \leq \exp\left[\frac{\sigma^2 x^2}{2}(1 + xM)\right], \quad (6)$$

and combining (6) with (5) produces (4).

Corollary. *For* $0 \leq a \leq 2\sigma^2 n/M$ *we have*

$$P(S_n \geq a) \leq \exp\left[\frac{-a^2}{2n\sigma^2}\left(1 - \frac{Ma}{n\sigma^2}\right)\right]. \quad (7)$$

Proof. We use the "exponential form" (5.6) of Chebyshev's inequality, which, with the aid of (4), becomes

$$P(S_n \geq a) \leq e^{-ax}E(e^{xS_n}) \leq \exp\left[\frac{nx^2\sigma^2}{2}(1 + xM) - ax\right]. \quad (8)$$

Choosing $x = a/\sigma^2 n$ converts (8) into (7), and the restriction $x \leq 2/M$ necessary for (4) becomes $a \leq 2\sigma^2 n/M$ as stated. It should perhaps be pointed out that this choice of x was not arbitrary. We wish to get as strong a bound as possible out of (8), and when x is small the choice we made is close to the one which minimizes the right-hand side, and gives a simpler formula than the exact minimum.

Using (7), it is easy to obtain the following result:

Hardy and Littlewood's Estimate. *If* $|X_i| \leq M$ a.s., *then* $|S_n| = O(\sqrt{n \log n})$ *a.s.*

Proof. Choosing $a = c\sqrt{n \log n}$ in (7) yields

$$P(S_n \geq c\sqrt{n \log n}) \leq \exp\left[-\frac{c^2}{2\sigma^2}\log n(1 + o(1))\right], \quad (9)$$

and the sum of the right side on n converges provided $c^2 > 2\sigma^2$. Therefore, by the B.-C. lemma, for such values of c $S_n \geq c\sqrt{n \log n}$ occurs for only finitely many values of n (a.s.). The same thing is true of $-S_n$, since what we have proved also applies to the r.v.'s $\{-X_n\}$, and that establishes the estimate.

It is not possible to go much further by finding still better upper bounds than (7), since that one is already very near to the truth.   The next step forward comes through realizing that events like $\{S_n \geq c \sqrt{n \log n}\}$ are highly correlated, so that the sum of all their probabilities, no matter how well each of the latter is estimated, does not give a good guide to the probability of the union or lim sup. To get around this we will find a way to handle the terms in large groups, so that only a subseries of the probabilities needs to converge in order to apply the B.-C. lemma. This is the second trick mentioned above. The means of carrying it out are found in an inequality which is similar to Kolmogorov's inequality of Section 8, but which provides a bound in terms of the distribution of S_n instead of explicitly.

Lemma 2. *Assuming only that $X_1, \ldots, X_n$ are independent with means 0 and variances σ^2, we have for any $a \geq 0$*

$$P(\max_{i \leq n} S_i \geq a) \leq 2P(S_n \geq a - \sqrt{2n\sigma^2}). \qquad (10)$$

Proof. Once again we define events A and A_j almost as in (8.4), but this time without absolute values:

$$A = \{\omega: \max_{i \leq n} S_i \geq a\}, \qquad \text{and for } j \leq n$$

$$A_j = \{\omega: S_i < a \text{ for } i < j, S_j \geq a\}. \qquad (11)$$

Again A_j are disjoint with union A. Now we write

$$P(A) = P(A \cap \{S_n \geq a - \sqrt{2n\sigma^2}\})$$
$$+ P(A \cap \{S_n < a - \sqrt{2n\sigma^2}\}), \qquad (12)$$

and noting that the first term is obviously not greater than $P(S_n \geq a - \sqrt{2n\sigma^2})$, we proceed to study the second. But

$$P(A_j \cap \{S_n < a - \sqrt{2n\sigma^2}\})$$
$$\leq P(A_j \cap \{|S_n - S_j| \geq \sqrt{2n\sigma^2}\}),$$

and using independence to factor the last term, and then Chebyshev's inequality in its common form (5.5), we get

$$P(A_j \cap \{S_n < a - \sqrt{2n\sigma^2}\}) \leq P(A_j) \frac{(n-j)\sigma^2}{2n\sigma^2} \leq \tfrac{1}{2}P(A_j).$$

Summing on j yields the bound

$$P(A \cap \{S_n < a - \sqrt{2n\sigma^2}\}) \leq \tfrac{1}{2}P(A). \qquad (13)$$

Combining (12) and (13) gives

$$P(A) \leq P(S_n \geq a - \sqrt{2n\sigma^2}) + \tfrac{1}{2}P(A),$$

which is the same as (10).

Khintchine's Estimate (Part i). *Assume again that* $|X_i| \leq M$ *a.s. Then*

$$P\left(\limsup_{n \to \infty} \frac{|S_n|}{\sqrt{n \log \log n}} \leq \sqrt{2}\,\sigma\right) = 1. \tag{14}$$

Proof. We will define $a(n) = (2\sigma^2 n \log \log n)^{1/2}$; the desired conclusion (14) amounts to showing that $|S_n| \leq (1 + \epsilon)a(n)$ for all large n (a.s.) whatever $\epsilon > 0$ we pick. Choose any $\gamma > 0$, and let $n_k = [(1 + \gamma)^k]$ define a roughly geometric sequence of positive integers.[8] From Lemma 2,

$$P(\max_{i \leq n_k} S_i \geq ca(n_k)) \leq 2P(S_{n_k} \geq ca(n_k) - \sqrt{2n_k\sigma^2})$$

where c is any constant greater than 1. Since $a(n)$ is of a larger order of magnitude than $\sqrt{n}$, the right-hand side can be written $2P(S_{n_k} \geq ca(n_k)[1 - o(1)])$. Applying (7), we have

$$P(\max_{i \leq n_k} S_i \geq ca(n_k)) \leq 2 \exp\left[-c^2 \log \log n_k(1 - o(1))\right]. \tag{15}$$

But $\log \log n_k$ is asymptotic to $\log k$, and so it is apparent that the sum (on k) of the right side of (15) is finite. Hence by the B.-C. lemma we are (almost) sure that

$$\max_{i \leq n_k} \{S_i\} < ca(n_k) \text{ for all large } k. \tag{16}$$

It is easy to see that (16) gives what we want. In particular it implies that, for all large k, if $n_{k-1} < i \leq n_k$ then

$$\frac{S_i}{\sqrt{i \log \log i}} \leq \frac{ca(n_k)}{\sqrt{n_{k-1} \log \log n_{k-1}}}.$$

---

[8] Here $[x]$ means the greatest integer $\leq x$.

But the right-hand side tends to $\sqrt{2\sigma^2 c^2(1+\gamma)}$, and so for any $\eta > 0$ if i is large enough we have

$$\frac{S_i}{\sqrt{i \log \log i}} \leq \sqrt{2\sigma^2 c^2(1+\gamma)} \,(1+\eta).$$

Since each of the factors c, $(1+\gamma)$ and $(1+\eta)$ can be chosen as close to 1 as desired, this establishes (14) with S_n instead of $|S_n|$. As before, the same proof applies to $-S_n$, and so (14) holds as stated.

    Problem 2. Using Lemma 2 and the "second trick" above, together with the moment estimates (3), obtain the Hardy-Littlewood bound without using Lemma 1. How much better can one do this way?

Equation (14) is a part of the "law of the iterated logarithm"; the remainder consists in showing that $\sqrt{2}\,\sigma$ is a.s. not greater than the lim sup in question. This can be done much as was the proof above, once the essential upper bound (7) has been replaced with an equally effective lower bound. Such a bound can be stated as follows:

Lemma 3. *Assume* $|X_i| \leq M$ *a.s. Let* a_n *be real numbers such that* $(a_n/\sqrt{n}) \to +\infty$, *but* $a_n = o(n)$. *Then for any* $\epsilon > 0$ *if* n *is large enough*

$$P(S_n > a_n) > \exp\left[\frac{-a_n{}^2}{2n\sigma^2}\,(1+\epsilon)\right]. \tag{17}$$

    Remarks. The analogous upper bound is, of course, a special case of (7). We will not prove Lemma 3, for the argument is somewhat tedious and enough is enough. (A proof, under the present assumptions, can be found in Khintchine's monograph [Kh], pp. 62–65.) For Bernoulli trials, Lemma 3 (and the whole law of the iterated logarithm) is nicely proved in [F]. There is one other important special case in which (17) can be obtained quite easily:

    Problem 3. Prove (17) and the corresponding upper bound in case the X_i have the *normal distribution*

$$P(X_i \leq x) = \frac{1}{\sqrt{2\pi}\,\sigma} \int_{-\infty}^{x} e^{-u^2/2\sigma^2}\, du. \tag{18}$$

(Hint: the crucial fact is that the sum of normally distributed, independent r.v.'s has itself a normal distribution.)

Finally, we will sketch the proof of the lower bound for S_n:

Khintchine's Estimate (Part ii). *Let the random variables X_i have variance σ^2 and satisfy the conclusion of Lemma 3 as well as the upper bound (14). Then*

$$P\left(\limsup_{n\to\infty} \frac{S_n}{\sqrt{n \log\log n}} \geq \sqrt{2}\,\sigma\right) = 1. \qquad (19)$$

Proof. Let $a(n) = (2\sigma^2 n \log\log n)^{1/2}$ once again, and take $n_k = [B^k]$ for some $B > 1$; we write B instead of $1 + \gamma$ to suggest that large values will be the useful ones this time. Let $c < 1$ and consider the events

$$A_k = \{\omega: S_{n_k} - S_{n_{k-1}} \geq ca(n_k - n_{k-1})\}.$$

Using (17) we have for large k

$$P(A_k) \geq \exp\left[-c^2(1 + \epsilon) \log\log(n_k - n_{k-1})\right]$$
$$\geq k^{-c^2(1+\epsilon)(1+o(1))}, \qquad (20)$$

so that $\Sigma P(A_k) = \infty$ provided we choose an ϵ for which $c^2(1 + \epsilon) < 1$. Since the events A_k are independent, it follows by B.-C. (ii) that an infinite number of them must occur a.s. Thus for arbitrarily large k we have

$$S_{n_k} \geq c(2\sigma^2(n_k - n_{k-1}) \log\log(n_k - n_{k-1}))^{1/2} + S_{n_{k-1}}. \qquad (21)$$

Since c is arbitrarily close to 1, this is almost what we need. By (14), the extra term $S_{n_{k-1}}$ on the right side is greater than $-2(2\sigma^2 n_{k-1} \log\log n_{k-1})^{1/2}$ for all large k, and it is easy to check that

$$(n_k - n_{k-1}) \log\log(n_k - n_{k-1}) \sim \left(1 - \frac{1}{B}\right) B^k \log k$$
$$\sim \left(1 - \frac{1}{B}\right) n_k \log\log n_k.$$

Combining these things with (21) yields for any $\delta > 0$

$$S_{n_k} \geq (2\sigma^2 n_k \log\log n_k)^{1/2}[c\sqrt{1 - B^{-1}} - 2B^{-1/2}](1 - \delta) \qquad (22)$$

for arbitrarily large k (a.s.), and since $c < 1$, $B > 1$ and $\delta > 0$ can be chosen to make the last factors as close to 1 as desired, this proves (19). (In this case omitting the absolute value makes the conclusion stronger.)

Remarks. By a truncation argument somewhat related to that which we used for the strong law of large numbers (but much more delicate), plus some refining of the above methods, it can be shown that in the identically-distributed case the finiteness of the second moment is sufficient for (14) and (19). It has also recently been proved that it is in a strong sense necessary. There are many extensions of the theorem even for the simplest cases and some quite different, powerful new methods of proof have been discovered; this circle of ideas which began more than 50 years ago still offers challenging unsolved problems.

3

Limiting Distributions and the
"Central Limit Problem"

12. WEAK CONVERGENCE OF MEASURES

In this chapter we will be considering theorems which assert that some random variable depending on a parameter n—usually a linear function of $X_1 + \cdots + X_n$ (X_i independent)—has a distribution which tends to a limit as $n \to \infty$. The present section is devoted to some generalities about the relevant notion of convergence of distributions. We will apply this concept only to measures on the real line in this chapter, but some discussion of more general cases is included; the reader is advised that weak convergence of measures on various function spaces has recently become quite important in the study of random processes.[1]

We begin with the basic definition. Let S be a metric space, and $\mathcal{S}$ the family of all Borel sets (that is, $\mathcal{S}$ is the smallest Borel field containing all the open subsets of S). Let $\{\mu_n\}$ be

---

[1] Section 26 gives an account of one such result.

a family of finite measures on $(S, \mathcal{S})$. Then we say that μ_n *converges weakly* to another such measure μ (written $\mu_n \Rightarrow \mu$) provided that

$$\lim_{n \to \infty} \int_S f \, d\mu_n = \int_S f \, d\mu \tag{1}$$

for every bounded, continuous, real-valued function f. Although the μ_n need not be probability measures (they will be in our applications), choosing $f \equiv 1$ shows that $\mu_n(S) \to \mu(S)$.

Problem 1. Let μ_n be a unit mass at the point x_n (that is, $\mu_n(E) = 1$ if $x_n \in E$, 0 otherwise). Show that $\mu_n \Rightarrow \mu$ provided $\lim x_n = x$ exists, and that μ must then be the unit mass at x. Prove the converse too (easy for Euclidean space, a bit harder for general S).

Problem 2. Let $S = [0, 1]$, and let μ_n be the discrete measure which puts mass $1/(n + 1)$ at each of the points $0, 1/n, 2/n, \ldots, n/n$. Prove that $\mu_n \Rightarrow \mu$, where μ is Lebesgue measure on $[0, 1]$.

It is not difficult to prove in general that there can be at most one measure μ for which $\mu_n \Rightarrow \mu$. In R^1, the determination of the limit takes on a more specific form:

Theorem 1. *Let μ_n, μ be finite measures on the Borel subsets of R^1, and let F_n, F be their respective distribution functions (Section 1). Then if $\mu_n \Rightarrow \mu$, we have*

$$\lim_{n \to \infty} F_n(x) = F(x) \tag{2}$$

for each x at which F is continuous.

Proof. Choose any $\epsilon > 0$ and consider the continuous function $g_\epsilon(t)$ which has the value 1 for $t \leq x$, 0 for $t \geq x + \epsilon$, and is linear in between. By the definition of weak convergence,

$$\int_{-\infty}^{\infty} g_\epsilon \, d\mu_n \to \int_{-\infty}^{\infty} g_\epsilon \, d\mu.$$

But it is obvious that

$$F_n(x) = \int_{-\infty}^{x} g_\epsilon \, d\mu_n \leq \int_{-\infty}^{\infty} g_\epsilon \, d\mu_n$$

and that

$$\int_{-\infty}^{\infty} g_\epsilon \, d\mu \leq F(x + \epsilon).$$

Combining these things yields

$$\limsup_{n \to \infty} F_n(x) \leq F(x + \epsilon), \tag{3}$$

and letting $\epsilon \to 0$ we obtain $F(x)$ as the upper bound (for any x) because of right continuity.

Now let $f_\epsilon(t)$ be 1 for $t \leq x - \epsilon$, 0 for $t \geq x$ and again linear between. Arguing much as before with f_ϵ instead of g_ϵ, we obtain

$$\liminf_{n \to \infty} F_n(x) \geq F(x - \epsilon). \tag{4}$$

Letting $\epsilon \to 0$ the lower bound becomes $F(x - 0)$, which is the same as the upper bound for $\limsup F(x)$ provided x is a continuity point.

Corollary. *If, on R^1, we have both $\mu_n \Rightarrow \mu$ and $\mu_n \Rightarrow \nu$, then $\mu = \nu$.*

The proof constitutes **Problem 3.** As remarked above, this uniqueness result is true in general, although Theorem 1 has meaning only in Euclidean spaces.

Problem 4. Generalize Theorem 1 to two dimensions.

Our next step will be to provide a partial converse to Theorem 1. The strict converse is false, as the following example shows: Let μ_n be unit mass at the point n, so that

$$F_n(x) = \begin{cases} 0 & \text{for } x < n, \\ 1 & \text{for } x \geq n. \end{cases}$$

Clearly, $F_n(x) \to 0$ for all x, and 0 is the distribution function of the "zero measure" μ_0, but μ_n is not weakly convergent to μ_0. The difficulty, of course, is that mass is "escaping to infinity." It turns out that in Euclidean spaces ruling out this possibility is all that is necessary. We give the proof for R^1:

Theorem 2. *Let $\{\mu_n\}$ be a sequence of finite Borel measures on R^1, μ another such measure, and F_n, F their respective distribution functions. If (2) holds at each x which is a continuity point of F, and if $\mu_n(R^1) \to \mu(R^1)$, then $\mu_n \Rightarrow \mu$.*

Proof. Let f be any bounded, continuous function on $(-\infty, \infty)$; we wish to prove that

$$\lim_{n \to \infty} \int_{-\infty}^{\infty} f \, d\mu_n = \int_{-\infty}^{\infty} f \, d\mu. \tag{5}$$

It is possible, for any $\epsilon > 0$, to choose an interval $[-A, A]$ such that each of the measures μ_n and μ gives weight at most ϵ to its complement. For, if B is taken so that $F(-B) \leq \epsilon/4$ and $-B$ is a continuity point of F, then $F_n(-B) \leq \epsilon/2$ for all large n. Similarly, if C is a continuity point and $F(\infty) - F(C) \leq \epsilon/4$, we will have $F_n(\infty) - F_n(C) \leq \epsilon/2$ for all large n. (The assumption that $\mu_n(R^1) \to \mu(R^1)$ must be used at this point.) We can then expand the interval until the bounds are true also for each of the finite number of n so far not covered; call the result $[-A, A]$. It is clear, therefore, that

$$\left| \int_{-\infty}^{\infty} f \, d\mu_n - \int_{-A}^{A} f \, d\mu_n \right| \leq M\epsilon \tag{6}$$

(and the same for μ), where M is an upper bound for $|f(x)|$. If we prove now that

$$\lim_{n \to \infty} \int_{-A}^{A} f \, d\mu_n = \int_{-A}^{A} f \, d\mu, \tag{7}$$

that will be enough, with (6), to establish (5).

Equation (7), written in terms of Riemann-Stieltjes integrals, is exactly the result usually called "Helly's second theorem." For completeness, we will sketch the proof. It is possible to approximate f uniformly in $[-A, A]$ by a step function s: for any $\delta > 0$, there are constants c_i and a_i such that

$$|f(x) - s(x)| \leq \delta \qquad \text{for } -A < x < A,$$

where

$$s(x) = \sum_{i=1}^{k-1} c_i \phi_{(a_i, \, a_{i+1}]}(x). \tag{8}$$

Here $(a_1, \ldots, a_k)$ forms a partition of $[-A, A]$, and it is even possible to assume that $a_1, \ldots, a_k$ are continuity points of F, since there are only a denumerable number of discontinuities to be avoided. If in each integral appearing in (7) f is replaced by the step function s, an error of at most $2\delta\mu(R^1)$ is introduced for large n. But (7) is obviously true for the step function, since

$$\int_{-A}^{A} s(x) \, d\mu_n = \sum_{i=1}^{k-1} c_i[F_n(a_{i+1}) - F_n(a_i)]$$

and $F_n(x) \to F(x)$ at continuity points. It follows, since δ can be taken arbitrarily small, that (7) holds for any continuous function, and the theorem is proved.

One way in which the notion of weak convergence can arise in probability is suggested by the following fact:

Problem 5. Show that if X_n, X are r.v.'s on a common probability space $(\Omega, \mathcal{B}, P)$ with distributions μ_n, μ, and if $X_n \to X$ in probability (Section 2), then $\mu_n \Rightarrow \mu$. (*Hint:* use Theorem 2.)

However, this is *not* the usual situation when weak convergence of distributions is found to occur, as we will see.

It is very useful to know when a weakly convergent subsequence of a family exists. A criterion can be obtained quite easily from Theorem 2.

Theorem 3. Let $\{\mu_n\}$ be finite Borel measures on R^1, and assume that $\{\mu_n(R^1)\}$ is bounded. If, for every $\epsilon > 0$, there exists a finite interval $[B_\epsilon, C_\epsilon]$ such that

$$\sup_n \mu_n(R^1 - [B_\epsilon, C_\epsilon]) \leq \epsilon, \tag{9}$$

then the family $\{\mu_n\}$ contains a weakly convergent subsequence.

Proof. First, we will choose a subsequence $\{\mu_{n'}\}$ for which $\lim F_{n'}(r)$ exists at every rational r. To see that this is possible we invoke the "diagonal method": order the rationals, and choose a subsequence $\{\mu_{n_1}\}$ such that $F_{n_1}(r_1)$ converges. Then choose a sub-subsequence $\{\mu_{n_2}\}$ for which the distribution functions converge at r_2 (as well as at r_1), and continue this process a countable number of times. Finally, let $\{\mu_{n'}\}$ consist of the "diagonal elements": use the first member of $\{\mu_{n_1}\}$, the second member of $\{\mu_{n_2}\}$, and so on. Under this construction, it is clear that the functions $F_{n'}$ must converge at each rational number.

For each rational r, we now have the existence of

$$\lim_{n' \to \infty} F_{n'}(r) = L(r). \tag{10}$$

It is clear that L is increasing and bounded, since the $F_{n'}$ are increasing and uniformly bounded; also, since $F_{n'}(x) \to 0$ uniformly as $x \to -\infty$ (an immediate consequence of (9)) we have $L(r) \to 0$ as $r \to -\infty$ through rationals. Define now, for any real x,

$$F(x) = \inf_{r>x} L(r). \qquad (11)$$

It is not difficult to see that F is nondecreasing, bounded, tends to 0 as $x \to -\infty$, and is right-continuous; in short, it is a distribution function. Let μ be the corresponding Borel measure; we will prove that $\mu_{n'} \Rightarrow \mu$.

In view of Theorem 2, we need only show that $\mu_{n'}(R^1) \to \mu(R^1)$ and that $F_{n'}(x) \to F(x)$ at continuity points of F. The first of these things is very easy, for the limits

$$\lim_{x \to -\infty} F_{n'}(x) = 0, \qquad \lim_{x \to +\infty} F_{n'}(x) = \mu_{n'}(R^1)$$

hold uniformly in view of (9) as we have already pointed out, and it follows that $F(-\infty) = 0$ and $F(+\infty) = \lim_{n'} \mu_{n'}(R^1)$.

Now let x be a fixed point at which F is continuous. For any rational number $r > x$, we have

$$\limsup_{n' \to \infty} F_{n'}(x) \leq \lim_{n' \to \infty} F_{n'}(r) = L(r) \leq F(r).$$

If instead we take $r \leq x$ we get

$$\liminf_{n' \to \infty} F_{n'}(x) \geq \lim_{n' \to \infty} F_{n'}(r) = L(r) \geq F(r - \epsilon)$$

for any $\epsilon > 0$. From these estimates it is clear (using continuity) that $F_{n'}(x) \to F(x)$, and the theorem follows.

Remarks. If the measures $\{\mu_n\}$ are concentrated entirely on some finite interval $[B, C]$, Theorem 3 becomes "Helly's first theorem" or "selection principle." (To obtain $\mu_{n'} \Rightarrow \mu$, Helly's second theorem is needed also.) The conclusion of Theorem 3 can obviously be strengthened to assert that every infinite subfamily of $\{\mu_n\}$ must contain a (weakly) convergent subsequence; we then say that $\{\mu_n\}$ is *conditionally compact*.[2] The generalization of the theorem to any metric space S is easily stated: call a family $\{\mu_n\}$ of finite measures on $(S, \mathcal{S})$ *tight*, if for every

---

[2] The adjective "conditionally" refers to the fact that the limiting measure need not belong to the original family.

$\epsilon > 0$ there is a compact set K_ϵ such that

$$\sup_n \mu_n(S - K_\epsilon) \leq \epsilon. \tag{12}$$

Theorem (Yu. V. Prokhorov). *If $\{\mu_n\}$ is a tight family and if $\{\mu_n(S)\}$ is bounded, then $\{\mu_n\}$ is conditionally compact. Conversely, provided S is separable and complete these two conditions are also necessary.*

For R^1, tightness of $\{\mu_n\}$ reduces to (9), so that Theorem 3 is a special case. We do not give the proof in general (see [2]).

Problem 6. Show in the case of R^1 that tightness and boundedness of $\{\mu_n(R^1)\}$ are necessary for conditional compactness.

13. THE MAXIMUM OF A SAMPLE

We will discuss briefly a class of limit theorems which are quite important in many applications, and yet simple to prove. Suppose that $X_1, X_2, \ldots$ are independent r.v.'s with the same distribution, and define

$$M_n = \max (X_1, X_2, \ldots, X_n). \tag{1}$$

It may be essential to know the probabilities with which different values of M_n will occur in the long run; that is, when n is large. In answering this question, it is intuitively clear that the character of the distribution of the X_i in the central part of its range is not important; all that matters is the way mass is distributed in the right-hand "tail."

The distribution function of M_n is easily found:

$$P(M_n \leq x) = P(X_i \leq x, i = 1, \ldots, n)$$
$$= \prod_{i=1}^{n} P(X_i \leq x) = F(x)^n, \tag{2}$$

where F is the common distribution function of the X_i. Under various assumptions on F, it is then easy to find the limiting distribution of a suitable linear function of M_n. For instance, *suppose that for some $\alpha > 0$*

$$\lim_{x \to +\infty} x^\alpha [1 - F(x)] = b > 0 \tag{3}$$

exists. *Then the distributions μ_n of the random variables $M_n/$* *$(bn)^{1/\alpha}$ have a weak limit μ as $n \to \infty$, whose distribution function is*

$$\lim_{n \to \infty} P(M_n \leq x(bn)^{1/\alpha}) = \mu\{(-\infty, x]\}$$

$$= \begin{cases} \exp(-x^{-\alpha}), & x > 0, \\ 0 & \text{for } x \leq 0. \end{cases} \quad (4)$$

The proof is simple. Using (2) and (3) we can write for any $x > 0$

$$P(M_n \leq (bn)^{1/\alpha}x) = F[(bn)^{1/\alpha}x]^n$$

$$= \left[1 - \frac{b}{bnx^\alpha} + o\left(\frac{1}{n}\right)\right]^n \to \exp(-x^{-\alpha}). \quad (5)$$

For $x \leq 0$, it is clear that $P(M_n \leq x(bn)^{1/\alpha}) \to 0$. The function defined by these limits (the last expression in (4)) is easily seen to be a probability distribution function which corresponds to some measure μ, and the convergence $\mu_n \Rightarrow \mu$ is then guaranteed by Theorem 2 of the previous section.

Two other possibilities will be left for the reader to complete:

Problem 1. Suppose that (3) is replaced by

$$\lim_{n \to +\infty} e^x[1 - F(x)] = b > 0. \quad (6)$$

Show that $\mu_n \Rightarrow \mu$, where μ_n is the distribution of $M_n - \log(nb)$ and

$$\mu\{(-\infty, x]\} = \exp(-e^{-x}), \qquad -\infty < x < \infty. \quad (7)$$

Problem 2. Suppose that the random variables X_i are bounded above by x_0 with probability one, and that instead of (3) we have for some $\alpha > 0$

$$\lim_{x \to x_0-} (x_0 - x)^{-\alpha}[1 - F(x)] = b > 0. \quad (8)$$

Show that $\mu_n \Rightarrow \mu$, where now μ_n is the distribution of $(nb)^{1/\alpha}(M_n - x_0)$ and

$$\mu\{(-\infty, x]\} = \begin{cases} \exp(-(-x)^\alpha) & \text{for } x < 0, \\ 1 & \text{for } x \geq 0. \end{cases} \quad (9)$$

It is a rather remarkable fact that we have now enumerated all the possibilities, in the following sense:

Theorem (B. V. Gnedenko). *Suppose there exist sequences of constants $a_n > 0$, b_n such that the distributions of $(M_n - b_n)/a_n$*

converge weakly to a limit ν which is not concentrated at one point. Let $G(x)$ be the distribution function of ν. Then there are constants $a > 0$, b such that $G(x) = H(ax + b)$, where H is one of the functions given in (4) or (7) or (9).

We will not give the proof, but refer to the elegant paper [3], where much more information can be found. For instance, the limiting distribution in (4) can be obtained under more general circumstances than (3), and the precise conditions are given in [3]. It should be noticed that even when (3) holds, we could have used different "normalizing constants" (a_n, b_n) instead of making the choice $((bn)^{1/\alpha}, 0)$ that actually led us to (4). For instance, the choice $((cn)^{1/\alpha}, (dn)^{1/\alpha})$ also leads to a limiting distribution, related to that of (4) by a linear change of variable. Two distributions so related are said to be *of the same type.* According to Gnedenko's theorem, then, such rather trivial changes in the limits are the only ones possible. We will encounter things analogous to these later on when we study sums, rather than maxima, of independent variables, and the notion of "type" will then be discussed in more detail.

14. CHARACTERISTIC FUNCTIONS

The most important problems about limiting distributions arise in determining the distribution of sums $X_1 + \cdots + X_n = S_n$ of independent random variables suitably "normalized," when n is large. The result in the case of Bernoulli trials is given by the famous "De Moivre-Laplace limit theorem" and may be stated as follows: *Let X_1, X_2, . . . be independent random variables, each taking the values* 1 *or* 0 *with probability* p *or* $1 - p = q$ *respectively* ($p \neq 0$ *or* 1). *Then as* $n \to \infty$ *the distribution of* $(S_n - np)/\sqrt{npq}$ *converges weakly to the "normal distribution," whose distribution function is*

$$\Phi(x) = \frac{1}{\sqrt{2\pi}} \int_{-\infty}^{x} e^{-u^2/2}\,du. \tag{1}$$

By virtue of Theorems 12.1 and 12.2, this weak convergence is the same as the relation

$$\lim_{n \to \infty} P\left(\frac{S_n - np}{\sqrt{npq}} \leq x\right) = \Phi(x) \qquad \text{for all } x; \tag{2}$$

(2) is the usual way of stating the theorem. This result and many generalizations of it are known as "central limit theorems."

The distribution function of S_n is obtained from those of the X_i by repeated convolution (Section 3), an operation which is usually very difficult to carry out directly. In certain cases this function can be found explicitly for all n, and then a direct evaluation of the limit analogous to (2) becomes feasible. For the Bernoulli case, of course, S_n has the binomial distribution (5.2), and a careful analysis of the terms with the aid of Stirling's formula will yield (2). (Such a proof is given in [F].) Other laws for the X_i under which explicit calculation of the distribution of S_n is feasible include the Poisson, exponential, and normal. But to obtain general theorems some other approach is required. One method is to calculate the moments of S_n, find their asymptotic behavior, and use it to obtain the limit of the distribution of $(S_n - b_n)/a_n$. This was the way in which Chebyshev first proved a very general analogue of (2). We will, however, follow another line introduced by Lyapunov around 1900 and which has been very widely applied since.

Let X be any random variable. The function ϕ (or ϕ_X if we wish to be explicit) defined by

$$\phi(\lambda) = E(e^{i\lambda X}), \tag{3}$$

which makes sense at least for all real λ, is called the *characteristic function* of X.[3] We can (see Section 2) also write

$$\phi(\lambda) = \int_{R^1} e^{i\lambda x}\, d\mu = \int_{-\infty}^{\infty} e^{i\lambda x}\, dF(x), \tag{4}$$

where μ and F are respectively the distribution (measure) and the distribution function of X; the last integral can be taken in the Riemann-Stieltjes sense since $e^{i\lambda x}$ is continuous.

Problem 1. Show that $\phi(0) = 1$, that $\left|\phi(\lambda)\right| \leq 1$ for all real λ, and that ϕ is uniformly continuous on the real line.

If $X_1, \ldots, X_n$ are independent, so are $\{e^{i\lambda X_j}\}$ and by Theorem 3.1 and its extension to several factors we have

$$\phi_{S_n}(\lambda) = E(e^{i\lambda(X_1 + \cdots + X_n)}) = \prod_{j=1}^{n} E(e^{i\lambda X_j}) = \prod_{j=1}^{n} \phi_{X_j}(\lambda). \tag{5}$$

[3] We will always regard ϕ as a function with domain the real line only.

It is this relation which makes characteristic functions an especially valuable tool for proving central limit theorems, since it provides a grip on the distribution of S_n when that of each X_j is known. Analytically, of course, a characteristic function is just the Fourier (Stieltjes) transform of a distribution function, and (5) expresses the fact that the transform of a convolution is the product of the transforms.

To see how characteristic functions can be used, we will next outline a proof of the De Moivre–Laplace theorem with their aid. It is first necessary to find the characteristic function of the normal distribution. For later use, we will take a normal distribution with arbitrary variance σ^2, whose distribution function is

$$\Phi_\sigma(x) = \frac{1}{\sqrt{2\pi}\,\sigma} \int_{-\infty}^{x} e^{-u^2/2\sigma^2}\, du. \tag{6}$$

(It is easy to check (see [F]) that this is indeed a distribution function having mean 0 and variance σ^2.) The result is

$$\phi(\lambda) = \int_{-\infty}^{\infty} e^{i\lambda x}\, d\Phi_\sigma(x) = e^{-\sigma^2\lambda^2/2}. \tag{7}$$

Problem 2. Derive (7). (*Hint:* Write ϕ as a Riemann integral and complete the square in the exponent. The resulting complex integral can be reduced, using Cauchy's theorem, to the real integral which expresses the fact that $\Phi_\sigma(+\infty) = 1$.)

Next, we find the characteristic function of $(S_n - np)/\sqrt{npq}$:

$$\phi_{X_j}(\lambda) = pe^{i\lambda} + q; \qquad \phi_{S_n}(\lambda) = (pe^{i\lambda} + q)^n;$$

and hence

$$\phi_n(\lambda) = E\big(e^{i\lambda(S_n - np)/\sqrt{npq}}\big) = e^{-i\lambda np/\sqrt{npq}}[pe^{i\lambda/\sqrt{npq}} + q]^n. \tag{8}$$

It is quite easy to pass to the limit in (8). The result is

$$\lim_{n\to\infty} \phi_n(\lambda) = e^{-\lambda^2/2} \qquad \text{for each } \lambda, \tag{9}$$

and the right-hand side, as we have seen, is the characteristic function of the normal distribution (1). The proof of the theorem, then, will be accomplished if we can show that (9) implies the weak convergence of the corresponding measures.

This will be done below. When the ground is prepared, much more general results will follow with very little extra labor.

Problem 3. Verify (9), using (8).

As a first step we need to show that the characteristic function of a distribution deserves its name—that is, that it uniquely determines the distribution. That is a consequence of the following inversion formula:

Theorem 1. *Let ϕ and F be respectively the characteristic and distribution functions of a probability measure on R^1. Let $\alpha < \beta$ be two points at which F is continuous. Then*

$$F(\beta) - F(\alpha) = \lim_{\sigma \to 0} \frac{1}{2\pi} \int_{-\infty}^{\infty} \phi(\lambda) e^{-\sigma^2 \lambda^2 / 2} \frac{e^{-i\lambda\beta} - e^{-i\lambda\alpha}}{-i\lambda} \, d\lambda. \quad (10)$$

Proof. First, we shall give some motivation. If the measure in question has a density $f(x)$, we can write

$$\phi(\lambda) = \int_{-\infty}^{\infty} e^{i\lambda u} f(u) \, du. \quad (11)$$

Then if $\phi \in L_1$ and if the interchange of integrations could be justified we would have

$$\frac{1}{2\pi} \int_{-\infty}^{\infty} e^{-i\lambda x} \phi(\lambda) \, d\lambda = \frac{1}{2\pi} \int_{-\infty}^{\infty} e^{-i\lambda x} \int_{-\infty}^{\infty} e^{i\lambda u} f(u) \, du \, d\lambda$$

$$= \frac{1}{2\pi} \int_{-\infty}^{\infty} f(u) \int_{-\infty}^{\infty} e^{-i\lambda(x-u)} \, d\lambda \, du;$$

recognizing the inner integral (with the factor $1/2\pi$) as the "Dirac delta function" the whole thing reduces to $f(x)$. What must be done to make sense out of this? There may, of course, not be a density f satisfying (11), and even if there is one, ϕ need not be integrable nor is the switching of integrals allowed. All of these difficulties can be overcome at once if we convolve the distribution function F with a normal distribution having mean 0 and variance σ^2. If σ is very small, this has little effect on F, yet it introduces just the needed convergence factor to aid the analysis.

Let us write $F_\sigma = F * \Phi_\sigma$ for the convolution (in the sense of (3.12)) of F with the function Φ_σ defined in (6), and let ϕ_σ

be the corresponding characteristic function. We can think of F_σ and ϕ_σ as obtained from the sum of two independent random variables with distributions F and Φ_σ. It is clear from (5) and (7) that

$$\phi_\sigma(\lambda) = e^{-\sigma^2\lambda^2/2}\phi(\lambda),$$

and since $|\phi| \leq 1$ this function is integrable. We can therefore write

$$\frac{1}{2\pi}\int_{-\infty}^{\infty} e^{-i\lambda x}\phi_\sigma(\lambda)\,d\lambda = \frac{1}{2\pi}\int_{-\infty}^{\infty} e^{-i\lambda x}e^{-\sigma^2\lambda^2/2}\int_{-\infty}^{\infty} e^{i\lambda u}\,dF(u)\,d\lambda.$$

This double integral *is* absolutely convergent, and Fubini's theorem justifies rewriting it in the form

$$\int_{-\infty}^{\infty}\frac{1}{2\pi}\int_{-\infty}^{\infty} e^{i\lambda(u-x)}e^{-\sigma^2\lambda^2/2}\,d\lambda\,dF(u) = \int_{-\infty}^{\infty} A(u, x)\,dF(u).$$

Now, the inner integral—the factor $A(u, x)$—can be evaluated easily, for it is just the characteristic function of a normal distribution with variance $1/\sigma^2$, evaluated at $(u - x)$ and multiplied by the constant factor $1/\sqrt{2\pi}\,\sigma$. From (7) we then have

$$A(u, x) = \frac{1}{\sqrt{2\pi}\,\sigma}e^{-(u-x)^2/2\sigma^2},$$

so that

$$\frac{1}{2\pi}\int_{-\infty}^{\infty} e^{-i\lambda x}\phi_\sigma(\lambda)\,d\lambda = \int_{-\infty}^{\infty}\frac{1}{\sqrt{2\pi}\,\sigma}e^{-(u-x)^2/2\sigma^2}\,dF(u). \quad (12)$$

But the right-hand side is the density of F_σ (Section 3). Thus, for any distribution convolved with a normal one, the formula arrived at through heuristic reasoning above is rigorously true.

If we integrate both sides of (12) from α to β, knowing that the right-hand side is $F_\sigma'(x)$, the result can be expressed as

$$F_\sigma(\beta) - F_\sigma(\alpha) = \frac{1}{2\pi}\int_{-\infty}^{\infty} \phi(\lambda)e^{-\sigma^2\lambda^2/2}\frac{e^{-i\lambda\beta} - e^{-i\lambda\alpha}}{-i\lambda}\,d\lambda. \quad (13)$$

(This interchange of integrals is obviously all right.) It is clear, therefore, that the theorem will be established as soon as we prove that

$$\lim_{\sigma\to 0+} F_\sigma(x) = F(x) \quad (14)$$

at each x for which F is continuous. To show this, recall that

$$F_\sigma(x) = P(X \leq x - Y_\sigma),$$

where Y_σ is independent of X (that is of no importance) and has mean 0 and variance σ. It follows from Chebyshev's inequality that given any $\epsilon > 0$, for all small enough values of σ

$$P(|Y_\sigma| \geq \epsilon) \leq \epsilon.$$

As a result we have, for such σ,

$$P(X \leq x - Y_\sigma) \leq P(X \leq x - Y_\sigma, |Y_\sigma| < \epsilon) + \epsilon$$
$$\leq F(x + \epsilon) + \epsilon,$$

and also

$$P(X \leq x - Y_\sigma) \geq P(X \leq x - \epsilon, |Y_\sigma| \leq \epsilon)$$
$$\geq P(X \leq x - \epsilon) - \epsilon = F(x - \epsilon) - \epsilon.$$

Combining these upper and lower bounds, it is clear that (14) holds at continuity points and the theorem is proved.

Problem 4.   If β, for instance, is not a continuity point of F, show that the limit in (10) still exists, but that $F(\beta)$ on the left side should be replaced by $|F(\beta+) + F(\beta-)|/2$.   (The same modification applies to α, of course.)

Since a probability distribution is uniquely determined by the values of its distribution function at continuity points, we have immediately this result.

Corollary 1.   *Two probability measures on Borel sets of* R^1 *with the same characteristic function are identical.*

Problem 5.   Use characteristic functions to verify that the sum of independent, normally distributed r.v.'s is again normal.

Corollary 2.   *If* $\phi(\lambda)$ *is the characteristic function of a measure* μ, *and if* $\phi \in L_1$ $(-\infty < \lambda < \infty)$, *then* μ *is absolutely continuous and its density is given by the integral*

$$f(x) = \frac{1}{2\pi} \int_{-\infty}^{\infty} e^{-i\lambda x} \phi(\lambda) \, d\lambda. \tag{15}$$

Proof.   Since $\phi \in L_1$, we can use the dominated convergence theorem to take the limit in (10) under the integral sign; the result is

$$F(\beta) - F(\alpha) = \frac{1}{2\pi} \int_{-\infty}^{\infty} \phi(\lambda) \frac{e^{-i\lambda\beta} - e^{-i\lambda\alpha}}{-i\lambda} \, d\lambda. \quad (16)$$

But the function $f(x)$ given in (15) is continuous, and it is clear from (16) that

$$\int_{\alpha}^{\beta} f(x) \, dx = F(\beta) - F(\alpha).$$

It is easy to conclude that $f(x) = F'(x)$ everywhere.

Problem 6.   (The Cauchy distribution.)   Show that the function

$$f(x) = \frac{1}{\pi} \frac{c}{c^2 + x^2}, \qquad c > 0, \quad (17)$$

is the density of a probability distribution with characteristic function $\phi(\lambda) = \exp(-c|\lambda|)$. If $X_1, \ldots, X_n$ are independent Cauchy distributed r.v.'s with the same c, what is the distribution of S_n/n?

Our final preliminary task is to study the continuity of the correspondence between distributions and characteristic functions. It is obvious from the definition of weak convergence that if $\mu_n \Rightarrow \mu$, then $\phi_n(\lambda) \to \phi(\lambda)$ for each real λ; the harder (and more useful) step is to establish a converse. If $\phi_n \to \phi$, and the latter is known to be a characteristic function, we could proceed by passing to the limit $n \to \infty$ under the integral sign in (13) for each fixed σ. However, by a somewhat different approach an even more general and useful result can be obtained.

Theorem 2.   *Let μ_n be probability distributions on R^1 and ϕ_n their characteristic functions. Suppose that*

$$\lim_{n \to \infty} \phi_n(\lambda) = \phi(\lambda) \text{ exists}, \qquad -\infty < \lambda < +\infty, \quad (18)$$

and that ϕ is continuous at the point $\lambda = 0$. Then there exists a probability distribution μ which has ϕ as its characteristic function, and $\mu_n \Rightarrow \mu$.

Proof.   The continuity of $\phi(\lambda)$ implies that the measures $\{\mu_n\}$ form a tight family (that is, satisfy (12.9)). To see this, we will first prove a simple result:

Lemma. *Let X be a random variable with characteristic function ψ. Then for any $u > 0$*

$$P\left(|X| > \frac{2}{u}\right) \leq \frac{1}{u} \int_{-u}^{u} [1 - \psi(\lambda)] \, d\lambda. \tag{19}$$

To establish (19), note first that the right-hand side can be written in the form

$$\frac{1}{u} \int_{-u}^{u} \int_{-\infty}^{\infty} (1 - e^{i\lambda x}) \, dF(x) \, d\lambda,$$

where F is the distribution of X. Interchanging the order of integration, this expression simplifies to

$$2 \int_{-\infty}^{\infty} \left(1 - \frac{\sin ux}{ux}\right) dF(x)$$

(and so it is necessarily real). Since the integrand is never negative, we can now obtain the estimate we seek as follows:

$$\frac{1}{u} \int_{-u}^{u} [1 - \psi(\lambda)] \, d\lambda \geq 2 \int_{-\infty}^{-2/u} + 2 \int_{2/u}^{+\infty} \left(1 - \frac{\sin ux}{ux}\right) dF(x)$$

$$\geq 2 \int_{-\infty}^{-2/u} + 2 \int_{2/u}^{+\infty} \left(1 - \frac{1}{|ux|}\right) dF(x)$$

$$\geq F\left(-\frac{2}{u}\right) + \left[1 - F\left(\frac{2}{u}\right)\right],$$

which proves the lemma.

Since the limiting function ϕ of (18) is continuous at 0 and has $\phi(0) = 1$, we can, given any $\epsilon > 0$, choose u so that

$$0 \leq \frac{1}{u} \int_{-u}^{u} [1 - \phi(\lambda)] \, d\lambda \leq \frac{\epsilon}{2}.$$

But then using the bounded convergence theorem it follows that

$$\frac{1}{u} \int_{-u}^{u} [1 - \phi_n(\lambda)] \, d\lambda \leq \epsilon \tag{20}$$

for all large n. Combining (19) and (20) we have essentially shown that the sequence $\{\mu_n\}$ is tight, for the interval $[-2/u, 2/u]$ can be enlarged to accommodate the finite set of measures for which (20) does not hold, and then we have precisely fulfilled (12.9).

It is easy to complete the proof of Theorem 2. By Theorem 12.3, the family $\{\mu_n\}$ has a subsequence weakly convergent to some limit μ. It follows that the characteristic functions of the subsequence converge to that of μ (at each λ), but since we assumed (18) we find that the limiting function ϕ must in fact be the characteristic function of μ. Now suppose that $\mu_n \Rightarrow \mu$ does not hold. By definition, for some bounded continuous f we have

$$\int_{R^1} f\, d\mu_n \nrightarrow \int_{R^1} f\, d\mu.$$

Choose a subsequence for which $\int f\, d\mu_{n'} \to L \neq \int f\, d\mu$. Then from *that* sequence a subsubsequence can be extracted (Theorem 12.3 again) which is weakly convergent to some measure ν. Since $\int f\, d\nu = L$, it is clear that $\nu \neq \mu$. However, by the argument we just used for μ, ν must also have ϕ for its characteristic function. This situation contradicts Corollary 1 above and so is impossible, which proves the theorem.

Problem 7. Using Theorem 2, show that $(S_n - n/2)/\sqrt{n}$ has a limiting normal distribution when $S_n = X_1 + \cdots + X_n$ and the X_i are independent r.v.'s each having the "uniform distribution" defined by

$$F(x) = \begin{cases} 0 & \text{if } x \leq 0, \\ x & \text{if } 0 \leq x \leq 1, \\ 1 & \text{if } x \geq 1. \end{cases} \tag{21}$$

Problem 8. Use Theorem 2 to prove Poisson's limit theorem: for each n, $X_i^{(n)}$ are independent r.v.'s, and $X_i^{(n)} = 1$ or 0 with probability $p_i^{(n)}$ or $1 - p_i^{(n)}$, $i = 1, \ldots, k(n)$. Assume that $\sum_{i=1}^{k(n)} p_i^{(n)} \to \mu$, $0 < \mu < \infty$, and that $\max_{i \leq k(n)} p_i^{(n)} \to 0$ as $n \to \infty$. Then $X_1^{(n)} + \cdots + X_{k(n)}^{(n)}$ has a limiting Poisson distribution with parameter μ.

15. CENTRAL LIMIT THEOREMS

With the preparations of the previous section behind us, it is very easy to prove a far-reaching generalization of the De Moivre-Laplace result:

Theorem 1. *Let* $X_1, X_2, \ldots$ *be independent r.v.'s with a common distribution having mean* μ *and variance* σ^2 ($m_2 < \infty$).

Then

$$P\left(\frac{S_n - n\mu}{\sqrt{n}} \le x\right) \Rightarrow \Phi_\sigma(x).^4 \tag{1}$$

Lemma. *Let X be any random variable with characteristic function ϕ. If $E(|X|^k) < \infty$ for some positive integer k, then ϕ has a continuous k'th derivative, and*

$$\phi^{(k)}(0) = i^k E(X^k). \tag{2}$$

Proof. Let $k = 1$. Then writing ϕ in the form (14.4) we easily get

$$\phi'(\lambda) = \lim_{h \to 0} \int_{-\infty}^{\infty} \frac{e^{ihx} - 1}{h} e^{i\lambda x} \, d\mu(x) \tag{3}$$

if the limit exists. The quotient approaches ix as $h \to 0$, so that interchanging limit and integral would give

$$\phi'(\lambda) = i \int_{-\infty}^{\infty} e^{i\lambda x} x \, d\mu. \tag{4}$$

But since

$$\left| e^{i\lambda x} \frac{e^{ihx} - 1}{h} \right| \le |x| \qquad (\lambda \text{ real})$$

and $|x|$ is integrable $(d\mu)$ by assumption, the dominated convergence theorem is applicable to justify the interchange and prove (4). If the kth moment is defined, the process can be repeated k times in exactly the same way. Setting $\lambda = 0$ at the end yields (2).

Remark. Although we will not prove it now, it will sometimes be useful to know that the converse assertion—that the existence of $\phi^{(k)}(0)$ implies that of $E(|X|^k)$—is true for even k but can fail when k is odd.

Proof of Theorem 1. We can assume that $\mu = 0$ with no loss of generality, for in any case that is true of the random variables $X_i - \mu$ whose partial sums are $S_n - n\mu$. If ϕ is the charac-

---

[4] The notation "$F_n \Rightarrow F$," applied to distribution functions, simply means the weak convergence of the corresponding measures as defined in Section 12 (or, equivalently, pointwise convergence at all the continuity points of the function F).

teristic function of X_i we have

$$E\left(\exp\left[i\lambda\,\frac{S_n}{\sqrt{n}}\right]\right) = \phi\left(\frac{\lambda}{\sqrt{n}}\right)^n \qquad (5)$$

by the multiplicative property. But using $\mu = 0$ and the lemma we can write the Taylor expansion

$$\phi(\lambda) = 1 - \frac{\sigma^2\lambda^2}{2} + o(\lambda^2), \qquad (6)$$

so that as $n \to \infty$

$$\phi\left(\frac{\lambda}{\sqrt{n}}\right)^n = \left[1 - \frac{\sigma^2\lambda^2}{2n} + o\left(\frac{1}{n}\right)\right]^n \to e^{-\sigma^2\lambda^2/2} \qquad (7)$$

for each fixed λ. The right-hand side of (7) is the characteristic function of Φ_σ (see Problem 14.2), which with (5) and the "continuity theorem" (Theorem 14.2) proves (1).

The theory of sums of independent random variables can be generalized to many Abelian groups other than the real line; the "harmonic analysis" of the group can play a role in the theory corresponding to that of the characteristic function in the classical case. There is a big difference between compact and noncompact groups, the former being in some respects simpler. In the following three problems we will study one of the simplest nontrivial examples: the multiplicative group of the complex numbers with absolute value one.

Let $X_1, X_2, X_3, \ldots$ be independent, identically distributed random variables with values in the group $\{e^{i\theta}\}$; they can be represented as $e^{2\pi i Y_n}$ where Y_n are independent and identically distributed with range $[0, 1]$. Let μ be the common distribution of the Y's; let $Z_n = X_1 \cdot X_2 \cdots X_n$. Introduce, as the analogue of the characteristic function, the Fourier coefficients of μ:

$$\phi(k) = \int_0^1 e^{2\pi i k x}\,d\mu(x) = E(X^k);$$

the "characteristic sequence" of Z_n is the n'th power of that of X.

Problem 1. Prove that the sequence $\{\phi(k)\}$ uniquely determines the distribution μ, provided that 0 and 1 are identified. (That is, μ is determined as a measure on the circle.)

Since we are really working on the circle, we interpret $\mu_n \Rightarrow \mu$ to mean $\int_0^1 f \, d\mu_n \to \int_0^1 f \, d\mu$ for every continuous f with $f(0) = f(1)$.

Problem 2. (The continuity theorem.) If μ_n has "characteristic function" ϕ_n, and $\lim_{n \to \infty} \phi_n(k) = \phi(k)$ exists for each k, show that $\mu_n \Rightarrow \mu$, where μ has characteristic function ϕ.

Problem 3. Show using the continuity theorem that "in general" the distribution of Z_n converges weakly to the uniform distribution on the circle (corresponding to Lebesgue measure on $[0, 1]$). Find the condition on μ which is necessary and sufficient for this convergence to hold, and interpret in group theoretic terms.

The problem of normal convergence, to which Theorem 1 is addressed, has an enormous literature and many ramifications. Perhaps one of the most natural questions is how our theorem generalizes if we drop the assumption that the r.v.'s have the same distribution. A very powerful result in this direction is that of Lindeberg (1922).

Theorem 2. *Let* $\{X_k\}$ *be independent with means* 0, *variances* $\{\sigma_k{}^2\}$, *and distributions* $\{\mu_k\}$, *and put* $B_n{}^2 = \Sigma_{k=1}^n \sigma_k{}^2 = \text{var } (S_n)$. *If for all* $\epsilon > 0$

$$\lim_{n \to \infty} \frac{1}{B_n{}^2} \sum_{k=1}^n \int_{|x| > \epsilon B_n} x^2 \, d\mu_k = 0, \qquad (8)$$

then the distribution of $(X_1 + \cdots + X_n)/B_n$ *converges weakly to the normal distribution (with* $\mu = 0$, $\sigma^2 = 1$).

Remarks. In the identically-distributed case of Theorem 1, the *Lindeberg condition* (8) reduces to the assertion that

$$\int_{|x| > \epsilon \sqrt{n}} x^2 \, d\mu \to 0,$$

which is obviously true since the second moment is finite. If the distributions vary but $\sigma_k{}^2$ is bounded away from zero, it is clear that the uniform integrability of $X_k{}^2$ is sufficient for (8). W. Feller has shown (1937) that condition (8) is in a sense necessary as well as sufficient: if $B_n{}^2 = \text{var } (S_n)$, if the distribution of S_n/B_n tends to the normal law (with $\sigma^2 = 1$), and if $\max_{k \leq n} \sigma_k/B_n \to 0$ so that each individual r.v. plays a negligible role, then (8) must hold.

Problem 4. Show that if, for some $\delta > 0$,

$$\lim_{n \to \infty} \frac{1}{B_n^{2+\delta}} \sum_{k=1}^{n} \int_{-\infty}^{\infty} x^{2+\delta} \, d\mu_k = 0,$$

then the Lindeberg condition must hold.

Proof of Theorem 2. We will consider the special case when each X_i has variance 1, leaving the fairly straight-forward extension to unequal variances for the reader. In this case, using the continuity theorem of the last section, the proof will be accomplished when we have shown that for all real λ

$$\lim_{n \to \infty} E\left(\exp\left[i\lambda \frac{S_n}{\sqrt{n}} \right] \right) = e^{-\lambda^2/2}. \tag{9}$$

Using the multiplicative property (14.5), we have at once

$$\log \phi_{S_n}\left(\frac{\lambda}{\sqrt{n}} \right) = \sum_{k=1}^{n} \log \phi_k\left(\frac{\lambda}{\sqrt{n}} \right), \tag{10}$$

where ϕ_k is the characteristic function of X_k. We will use the estimate $\log (1 + x) = x + O(|x|^2)$ for x near 0; to do this we need bounds on the quantity which plays the role of x, namely $\phi_k\left(\dfrac{\lambda}{\sqrt{n}} \right) - 1$. Now, for each k,

$$\phi_k\left(\frac{\lambda}{\sqrt{n}} \right) - 1 = \int_{-\infty}^{\infty} (e^{i\lambda x/\sqrt{n}} - 1) \, d\mu_k$$

$$= \int_{-\infty}^{\infty} \left(e^{i\lambda x/\sqrt{n}} - 1 - \frac{i\lambda}{\sqrt{n}} x \right) d\mu_k;$$

in writing the last expression we used the assumption that the means are 0. But the bound

$$\left| e^{i\alpha} - 1 - i\alpha \right| \leq \frac{\alpha^2}{2} \qquad (\alpha \text{ real}) \tag{11}$$

is easily derived from Taylor's theorem, and using it we get

$$\left| \phi_k\left(\frac{\lambda}{\sqrt{n}}\right) - 1 \right| \leq \int_{-\infty}^{\infty} \frac{\lambda^2 x^2}{2n} \, d\mu_k = \frac{\lambda^2}{2n}. \tag{12}$$

With the aid of (12) we have for each λ

$$\log \phi_k\left(\frac{\lambda}{\sqrt{n}}\right) = \phi_k\left(\frac{\lambda}{\sqrt{n}}\right) - 1 + O\left(\frac{1}{n^2}\right), \tag{13}$$

where the error term holds uniformly in k.

The next step is to estimate

$$\phi_k\left(\frac{\lambda}{\sqrt{n}}\right) - 1 + \frac{\lambda^2}{2n}$$

$$= \int_{-\infty}^{\infty} \left(e^{i\lambda x/\sqrt{n}} - 1 - \frac{i\lambda x}{\sqrt{n}} + \frac{\lambda^2 x^2}{2n}\right) d\mu_k. \tag{14}$$

Again, from Taylor's theorem we have

$$\left| e^{i\alpha} - 1 - i\alpha + \frac{\alpha^2}{2} \right| \leq \frac{|\alpha^3|}{3!} \qquad (\alpha \text{ real}), \tag{15}$$

which is a good bound when α is small. After taking absolute values in (14), choose $\epsilon > 0$ and divide the range of integration into the two parts $|x| \leq \epsilon \sqrt{n}$ and $|x| > \epsilon \sqrt{n}$. In the first part we will estimate the integrand with (15); in the second we use (11). The result is

$$\left| \phi_k\left(\frac{\lambda}{\sqrt{n}}\right) - 1 + \frac{\lambda^2}{2n} \right| \leq \frac{|\lambda^3|}{6n^{3/2}} \int_{|x| \leq \epsilon\sqrt{n}} |x|^3 \, d\mu_k$$

$$+ \frac{\lambda^2}{n} \int_{|x| > \epsilon\sqrt{n}} x^2 \, d\mu_k. \tag{16}$$

Replacing one factor x by its maximum, the first term is seen to be less than $|\lambda^3|\epsilon/6n$. Combining this modification of (16) with (13), we obtain

$$\left| \log \phi_k\left(\frac{\lambda}{\sqrt{n}}\right) + \frac{\lambda^2}{2n} \right| \leq \frac{|\lambda^3|\epsilon}{6n} + \frac{\lambda^2}{n} \int_{|x| > \epsilon\sqrt{n}} x^2 \, d\mu_k$$

$$+ O\left(\frac{1}{n^2}\right). \tag{17}$$

Finally it is time to sum from 1 to n, as in (10), and estimate the error:

$$\left| \log \phi_{S_n}\left(\frac{\lambda}{\sqrt{n}}\right) + \frac{\lambda^2}{2} \right| \leq \frac{|\lambda^3|\epsilon}{6} + O\left(\frac{1}{n}\right)$$

$$+ \frac{\lambda^2}{n} \sum_{k=1}^{n} \int_{|x|>\epsilon\sqrt{n}} x^2 \, d\mu_k. \quad (18)$$

Give any $\delta > 0$, choose ϵ so that the first term on the right is $\leq \delta$; then for all large n the whole bound can be held below 2δ. (At last we make use of the key hypothesis (8).) It is clear now that we have proved (9), from which the theorem follows.

Problem 5. Show that (8) implies $B_n \to \infty$ and $\max_{k \leq n} \sigma_k^2/B_n^2 \to 0$.

Problem 6. Discuss the modifications in the above proof which are necessary to prove Theorem 2 in general.

We shall mention, without details, a few of the many auxiliary results which accompany the central limit theorem. In order to make practical applications of almost any limit theorem, estimates of the rate of convergence are essential. The following theorem, due to Cramer, Berry, and Esseen, gives such information in the context of our first result:

Theorem. *Let X_1, X_2, . . . be independent with a common distribution having mean 0, variance σ^2, and finite third moment. Then there is a constant C such that*

$$\left| P\left(\frac{S_n}{\sqrt{n}} \leq x\right) - \Phi_\sigma(x) \right|$$

$$\leq \frac{CE(|X_1|^3)}{\sigma^3 \sqrt{n}}, \qquad -\infty < x < \infty.[5] \quad (19)$$

Under various additional conditions more precise results can be obtained. In particular, if higher moments are available the difference between the actual and the limiting distributions

[5] Although the smallest value of C which works for all distributions is not known, it is, at any rate, less than 3.

has an asymptotic development in which the l'th term depends on $m_1, \ldots, m_{l+2}$ and is of the order of $n^{-l/2}$. The basic idea for this expansion goes back to Chebyshev; see [GK] for a complete discussion.

Problem 7. Show that no bound of smaller order than $1/\sqrt{n}$ can hold in general in (19). (*Hint:* consider the Bernoulli case.)

Another modification of the central limit theorem (abbreviated c.l.t.) is to investigate the convergence of the density of $S_n/\sqrt{n}$, if it exists, to that of Φ_σ. This does *not* follow from the mere existence of a density for X_i, even in the identically distributed case, but the following is true:

Theorem. *If $X_1, X_2, \ldots$ are independent with a common distribution μ having mean 0 and variance σ^2, and if μ has a bounded density, then*

$$\lim_{n \to \infty} \sup_{-\infty < x < \infty} \left| \frac{d}{dx} P\left(\frac{S_n}{\sqrt{n}} \le x \right) - \frac{1}{\sqrt{2\pi}\,\sigma} e^{-x^2/2\sigma^2} \right| = 0. \quad (20)$$

Finally, we mention the "local limit theorem" for "lattice distributions." If the range of X_i is (a.s.) a subset of the integers the same is true of S_n, and it is desirable to be able to estimate the probability that S_n takes a particular value. (Actually, this is the way the De Moivre-Laplace theorem was first proved.) The characteristic function reduces in this case to a Fourier series, and finding the desired probability is equivalent to evaluating one of the coefficients of the series. A general theorem along these lines was discovered by Gnedenko and is explained nicely in his book [G]. Here again (and in the results about densities) there are, under stronger conditions, precise bounds and asymptotic expansions for the error terms which play an important role in many specific applications of the limit theorems.

16. SYMMETRIC STABLE LAWS

In 1920, Holtzmark raised and solved the following problem: If electrically charged particles are distributed "randomly" in space, what will be the distribution of the resulting electric field at a fixed point? About 1940 Chandrasekhar studied analogous problems concerning the gravitational field resulting from a random distribution of stars. We will now formulate a simplified, one-dimensional model in the spirit of these investigations.

Assume that n "stars" are located in the interval $[-n, n]$ on the real line. Their locations are independent, each being uniformly distributed in the interval. Each star has mass $m > 0$, and the gravitational constant is unity. The force which will be exerted on a unit mass at the origin (the field strength) is then

$$F_n = \sum_{i=1}^{n} \frac{m \ \text{sign} \ (X_i)}{X_i{}^2}, \tag{1}$$

where X_i is the coordinate of the i'th star. We will show now that the distributions of the random variables F_n have a weak limit as $n \to \infty$.

Let us compute the characteristic function of F_n. First, observe that since X_i is uniformly distributed, we have

$$E\left(\exp \left[i\lambda \ \frac{m \ \text{sign} \ (X_i)}{X_i{}^2} \right] \right) = \int_{-n}^{n} \exp \left[i\lambda \ \frac{m \ \text{sign} \ (x)}{x^2} \right] \frac{dx}{2n}$$
$$= \frac{1}{n} \int_{0}^{n} \cos \left(\frac{\lambda m}{x^2} \right) dx. \tag{2}$$

Because of independence, the characteristic function of F_n is the n'th power of this expression. Making some simple changes, it is not difficult to pass to the limit:

$$E(\exp [i\lambda F_n]) = \left\{ 1 - \frac{1}{n} \int_{0}^{n} \left[1 - \cos \left(\frac{\lambda m}{x^2} \right) \right] dx \right\}^n$$
$$= \left\{ 1 - \frac{1}{n} \int_{0}^{\infty} \left[1 - \cos \left(\frac{\lambda m}{x^2} \right) \right] dx + o \left(\frac{1}{n} \right) \right\}^n$$
$$\to \exp \left(- \int_{0}^{\infty} \left[1 - \cos \left(\frac{\lambda m}{x^2} \right) \right] dx \right).$$

By means of a change of variable in the integral, our result can finally be written as

$$\lim_{n \to \infty} E(\exp [i\lambda F_n]) = \exp (-c|\lambda|^{1/2}), \ c > 0. \tag{3}$$

Since the right side is continuous, by Theorem 14.2 it must be the characteristic function of a distribution to which the distributions of F_n are weakly convergent. It is not possible to express the distribution function in elementary terms, although a good deal is known about its properties.

Problem 1. Suppose that the inverse-square attraction in (1) were replaced by an inverse p'th-power attraction. Show that provided $0 < p^{-1} < 2$, (3) would be replaced by

$$\lim_{n \to \infty} E(\exp [i\lambda F_n]) = \exp (-c|\lambda|^{1/p}), \quad c > 0. \tag{4}$$

The distributions whose characteristic functions are given by the right side of (4) are called *stable laws*[6]; the parameter $1/p$ is the *index* of the law. If $p = 1$ we obtain Cauchy's distribution. The case where the index is 2—the normal law—is included also, although it does not arise in the above manner. In general, a distribution is said to be *stable* if it is not concentrated at one point and has the following property: *let X_1 and X_2 be independent r.v.'s with the given distribution, and let a_1 and a_2 be any positive constants. Then there exist $\alpha > 0$ and β (depending on a_1 and a_2) such that the r.v.*

$$X_3 = \frac{1}{\alpha} (a_1X_1 + a_2X_2 - \beta) \tag{5}$$

has once again the distribution in question. This may be paraphrased as asserting that the stable distributions are those which reproduce themselves up to a linear change of variable under the operation of convolution.

If $\phi(\lambda)$ is the characteristic function of X, the stable property implies that

$$\phi(a_1\lambda)\phi(a_2\lambda) = e^{i\lambda\beta}\phi(\alpha\lambda), \tag{6}$$

and because of the uniqueness theorem (6) is actually equivalent to (5). It is easy to verify that the "stable" characteristic function given in (4) does have property (6), so that our terminology is consistent.

As we shall see in the next section, there is a very close relationship between the class of stable laws and limit theorems for sums of independent r.v.'s. Before coming to that topic, however, we will try to gain a better idea of the extent of the class. Note that it is clear from their derivation that the stable

[6] The terms "law" and "distribution" are synonomous.

distributions we have found are symmetric about 0; we will show that there are no others with this property.

Theorem 1. *If $\phi(\lambda)$ is the characteristic function of a stable distribution which is symmetric about the origin, then there exists $c > 0$ and $\alpha \in (0, 2]$ such that*

$$\phi(\lambda) = e^{-c|\lambda|^\alpha}. \tag{7}$$

It is well to first clarify the role of symmetry:

Lemma 1. *A characteristic function is real if and only if the corresponding distribution is symmetric about 0.*

Proof. From the definition we have

$$\phi(\lambda) = \int_{-\infty}^{\infty} \cos \lambda x \, d\mu + i \int_{-\infty}^{\infty} \sin \lambda x \, d\mu; \tag{8}$$

since $\sin \lambda x$ is odd, it is obvious that symmetry of the distribution μ implies that ϕ is real. For the converse, first note that

$$\phi_{-X}(\lambda) = E(e^{-i\lambda X}) = \overline{\phi_X(\lambda)}. \tag{9}$$

Hence if ϕ_X is real, X and $-X$ have the same characteristic function and so, by the uniqueness theorem, the same distribution. This is equivalent to symmetry.

Proof of the theorem. Let $\phi(\lambda)$ be the characteristic function of a stable law which is symmetric about the origin. We will first show that $\phi(\lambda) = 0$ never holds (on the real line). Suppose the contrary. Then since ϕ is real, even, and continuous there must be a smallest positive λ_0 such that $\phi(\lambda_0) = 0$. Now because of (6) there is a positive number d such that

$$\phi^2(\lambda) = \phi(d\lambda). \tag{10}$$

If $d = 1$, for each λ either $\phi(\lambda) = 1$ or $\phi(\lambda) = 0$. By continuity it must always be $\phi(\lambda) = 1$, which contradicts our supposition. If $d < 1$, the choice $\lambda = \lambda_0$ in (10) shows that λ_0 was not the smallest 0; if $d > 1$, the choice $\lambda = \lambda_0/d$ has the same effect. Hence, the function ϕ has no zeros. Since it is real and continuous and $\phi(0) = 1$, it is clear that $\phi(\lambda) > 0$ for all λ and we can let $\psi(\lambda) = \log \phi(\lambda)$ with no ambiguity.

It is easy to see that the stability condition (6) translates into the assertion that for every positive a_1, a_2 there exists a positive $f(a_1, a_2)$ such that

$$\psi(a_1\lambda) + \psi(a_2\lambda) = \psi(f(a_1, a_2)\lambda); \qquad (11)$$

it is our object to find the general continuous solution of this functional equation. We will need the following fact:

Lemma 2. If $\psi(a\lambda) = \psi(b\lambda)$ for all λ, $a \geq b > 0$, then $a = b$.

Proof. Suppose $a \neq b$. Clearly, $\psi(\xi) = \psi((b/a)\xi)$ for all ξ, and iterating yields $\psi(\xi) = \psi((b/a)^n\xi)$. If we now let $n \to \infty$ and use continuity we find the degenerate case, and so necessarily $a = b$.

Returning to the solution of (11), we define a function $g > 0$ on the positive integers such that

$$n\psi(\lambda) = \psi(g(n)\lambda) \qquad (12)$$

for all λ. To obtain g, start with $g(1) = 1$ and proceed by induction:

$$n\psi(\lambda) = \psi(\lambda) + (n - 1)\psi(\lambda) = \psi(\lambda) + \psi(g(n - 1)\lambda),$$

so that, using (11), we can take $g(n) = f(1, g(n - 1))$. (Because of Lemma 2, g is in fact uniquely determined by (12).) From (12) we easily get

$$\psi(g(nm)\lambda) = nm\psi(\lambda) = n\psi(g(m)\lambda) = \psi(g(n)g(m)\lambda),$$

and another appeal to Lemma 2 shows that

$$g(mn) = g(m)g(n). \qquad (13)$$

Let us define $g(p/q) = g(p)/g(q)$, where p and q are positive integers. Because of (13), this gives a well-defined multiplicative function on all the positive rationals. It is easy to check that (12) now holds for rationals as well as integers, and this detail will be left to the reader.

Finally, suppose a sequence of rational numbers r_n tends to $x > 0$; we will show that $\lim g(r_n)$ exists. It is clear that

$$\lim_{n \to \infty} \psi(g(r_n)\lambda) = \lim_{n \to \infty} r_n\psi(\lambda) = x\psi(\lambda). \qquad (14)$$

This shows that $g(r_n)$ can not have 0 as a limit point, for if it did, the right side of (14) would have to be $\psi(0) = 0$. In the same way, working with r_n^{-1}, it can be seen that no subsequence of $g(r_n)$ can tend to ∞. Hence, $g(r_n)$ is bounded and has at least one limit point. But there cannot be two, say u and v, for then from (14) we could get $\psi(u\lambda) = \psi(v\lambda)$ which again contradicts Lemma 2. Hence $\lim g(r_n)$ exists, and we will call it $g(x)$. It does not depend on the particular sequence of rationals $r_n \to x$, for any two such sequences can be "interlaced," and the resulting new sequence must still yield a limit. It is now not difficult to verify that for all positive x, y we have

$$g(xy) = g(x)g(y), \qquad (15)$$

that (12) holds with any positive x replacing n, and that g is continuous on $(0, \infty)$.

Problem 2. Supply the steps to justify the last sentence.

Problem 3. Show that the general continuous solution of (15) is given by $g(x) = x^p$, p constant. (Similar things can be found in Courant's *Calculus*, Vol. 1.)

Let us return to (12), armed with the fact that $g(x) = x^p$, and substitute $x^{1/p}$ for n and 1 for λ. (We observe that since $g(x) > 0$, p is real.) The result is that for $x > 0$

$$\psi(x) = \psi(1)x^{1/p}. \qquad (16)$$

We know that ϕ, and hence ψ, is an even function, and so the general form (7) is established with $\alpha = 1/p$ and $c = -\psi(1)$. The condition $c > 0$ follows since $\phi(\lambda)$ is bounded and not identically 1, and $\alpha \neq 0$ is also assured for the latter reason. Continuity at 0 and $\phi(0) = 1$ obviously rule out values of $\alpha < 0$. It only remains to show that $\alpha \leq 2$, and the theorem will be proved.

The last step is accomplished as follows: if $\alpha > 2$, it is clear that $\phi''(0) = 0$. We have already remarked (without proof) that the existence of $\phi''(0)$ implies the finiteness of the second moment; in our case the moment must vanish. But this would again make our law degenerate, and a unit mass at 0 does not have (7) for its characteristic function. We conclude that (7) is not a characteristic function at all when $\alpha > 2$.

Problem 4. Show that if $\phi''(0)$ exists, so does $\int_{-\infty}^{\infty} x^2 \, dF$. (*Hint:* Since ϕ is real, we can write

$$\frac{-\phi''(0)}{2} = \lim_{h \to 0} \int_{-\infty}^{\infty} \frac{1 - \cos hx}{h^2} \, dF(x);$$

now apply Fatou's lemma.)

Remark. The general stable characteristic function can be identified similarly, but we will not do it. Roughly speaking, there are two new parameters, one of which measures the actual "skewness" of the law, the other arising simply by a translation. We refer to [GK] or to [F2] for the complete story, obtained by a different approach. The method above resembles that used by Paul Levy, the originator of the theory.

17. STABLE LAWS AND LIMIT THEOREMS

The problem answered by "central limit theorems"—to find conditions under which sums of independent r.v.'s have a limiting normal distribution—is ancient. It was, however, only relatively recently that many closely related questions have been raised. One of the first of these may be stated as follows: If the partial sums of a sequence of independent r.v.'s with the same distribution have (after normalization) *some* limiting distribution, what can the limit be? This problem was raised and solved by Paul Levy in the early 1930's; this and related more general results have immeasurably enriched probability theory.

The main goal of this section is to prove the following fact:

Theorem 1 (Levy). *Let X_1, X_2, . . . be independent r.v.'s with a common distribution and suppose that there exist constants $b_n > 0$ and a_n such that*

$$P\left(\frac{X_1 + \cdots + X_n - a_n}{b_n} \leq x\right) \Rightarrow F(x) \qquad (1)$$

for some distribution function F which does not represent a degenerate law.[7] Then F is stable.

Although the idea of the proof is quite simple, certain preparations are needed before it can be carried out rigorously. Some

[7] That is, a distribution concentrated at one point.

of these are of wider interest or are helpful conceptually, as we shall see. The first fact we establish is that convolution is a continuous operation with respect to weak convergence.

Lemma 1. *Suppose that F_n, F, G_n and G are all probability distribution functions, and that $F_n \Rightarrow F$ and $G_n \Rightarrow G$. Let "$*$" denote the operation of convolution. Then*

$$F_n * G_n \Rightarrow F * G. \tag{2}$$

Proof. Let ϕ_n, ϕ, ψ_n, ψ be the characteristic functions of the distributions F_n, F, G_n, G respectively. By the definition of "$\Rightarrow$" we have

$$\phi_n(\lambda) \to \phi(\lambda) \qquad \text{and} \qquad \psi_n(\lambda) \to \psi(\lambda)$$

for each λ, and hence

$$\phi_n(\lambda)\psi_n(\lambda) \to \phi(\lambda)\psi(\lambda) \tag{3}$$

also. But $\phi_n\psi_n$ $(\phi\psi)$ is the characteristic function of $F_n * G_n$ $(F * G)$, and so, in view of the continuity theorem (Section 14), the desired convergence (2) follows from (3).

Lemma 2. *Let F_n and G be probability distribution functions, a_n and b_n constants with $b_n > 0$, and suppose that*

$$F_n(b_n x + a_n) \Rightarrow G(x). \tag{4}$$

Suppose that α_n and β_n are constants such that

$$\lim_{n \to \infty} \frac{\beta_n}{b_n} = 1; \qquad \lim_{n \to \infty} \frac{\alpha_n - a_n}{b_n} = 0. \tag{5}$$

Then it is also the case that

$$F_n(\beta_n x + \alpha_n) \Rightarrow G(x). \tag{6}$$

Problem 1. Prove this lemma, using the fact that both (4) and (6) are equivalent to pointwise convergence at each x for which G is continuous.

We will say that two distribution functions F and G are *of the same type* if there exist constants a and b, $b > 0$, such that

$$F(bx + a) = G(x) \tag{7}$$

for all x. It is easy to see that this is an equivalence relation. Using the new terminology, the definition of a stable law may be paraphrased as follows: F is stable if the convolution of any two distributions of the same type as F is again of the same type as F. It follows that stability is a property which holds for all distributions of given type, or for none.

Problem 2. Verify that the above characterization of stable distributions is equivalent to that of the previous section.

It is fairly apparent that if (1) holds with a certain distribution F, any distribution of the same type as F could also be obtained by using different constants in place of b_n and a_n.

Problem 3. Prove the last statement, and exhibit suitable new constants.

Our next lemma establishes a converse. Like Lemma 2, it has nothing to do with sums of r.v.'s as such, and so is also relevant, for instance, to the study of limit laws for maxima which was touched upon earlier in Section 13.

Lemma 3. *Suppose that F_n, G, and H are probability distribution functions, and that*

$$F_n(x) \Rightarrow G(x) \qquad \text{and} \qquad F_n(b_n x + a_n) \Rightarrow H(x) \qquad (8)$$

where $b_n > 0$ and a_n are constants. Suppose also that neither G nor H is degenerate. Then G and H are of the same type.

Proof. We will first show that $\{b_n\}$ has a subsequence tending to a positive, finite limit b. If not, there is a subsequence for which either $b_{n'} \to 0$ or else $b_{n'} \to +\infty$. Suppose for the moment that $a_n \equiv 0$. Then in the case $b_{n'} \to 0$ it is easy to see from the fact $F_n \Rightarrow G$ that

$$H(x) = \lim_{n' \to \infty} F_{n'}(b_{n'} x) = \begin{cases} G(0+) & \text{if } x > 0, \\ G(0-) & \text{if } x < 0. \end{cases}$$

This is not possible, since the limit is not a probability distribution function at all unless G is degenerate. Similarly, if $b_{n'} \to +\infty$, we get

$$H(x) = \lim_{n' \to \infty} F_{n'}(b_{n'} x) = \begin{cases} 1 & x > 0, \\ 0 & x < 0, \end{cases}$$

which is itself degenerate.   Hence, the existence of $b_{n'} \to b > 0$ is established.

To remove the condition that $a_n \equiv 0$, we will use a trick closely related to one employed in proving the three series theorem (Section 9). If F is the distribution of a r.v. X, then $F^{(-)}$, by definition the distribution of $-X$, is essentially [8] $1 - F(-x)$. It is clear that $F_n \Rightarrow G$ implies $F_n^{(-)} \Rightarrow G^{(-)}$, and so, by Lemma 1, we have also

$$F_n * F_n^{(-)} \Rightarrow G * G^{(-)}$$

and

$$F_n(b_n x + a_n) * F_n^{(-)}(b_n x + a_n) \Rightarrow H * H^{(-)}.$$

However, it is easy to see that

$$F_n(b_n x + a_n) * F_n^{(-)}(b_n x + a_n) = F_n(b_n x) * F_n^{(-)}(b_n x),$$

since the a_n's represent translations that are made in both directions and so cancel.   Therefore the laws $F_n * F_n^{(-)}$ satisfy the hypothesis of the lemma with no translation terms a_n appearing in (8), and with the same constants b_n.   It follows from the first paragraph of the proof, then, that a subsequence $b_{n'}$ tends to $b > 0$.

Looking at the second part of (8) with n restricted to the subsequence n' ($b_{n'} \to b > 0$), we see that a_n cannot tend to $+\infty$ or $-\infty$ without causing H to be degenerate.   It is possible, therefore, to choose a subsequence n'' for which both

$$b_{n''} \to b \in (0, \infty) \qquad \text{and} \qquad a_{n''} \to a \in (-\infty, \infty).$$

Now, from the first part of (8) we know that

$$F_{n''}(bx + a) \Rightarrow G(bx + a),$$

while

$$F_{n''}(b_{n''} x + a_{n''}) \Rightarrow H(x).$$

It follows by Lemma 2 that $H(x) = G(bx + a)$, which is the same as the assertion of Lemma 3.

The last result ends the general preparations; we will prove one more lemma, but this one is aimed solely at the proof of Theorem 1.

---

[8] This is correct at continuity points, since $1 - F(-x)$ equals $P(-X < x)$ rather than $P(-X \le x)$ as we usually define a distribution function.

Lemma 4. *Under the conditions of Theorem 1, $b_n \to \infty$ and* $\lim \sup b_{n+1}/b_n = 1$.

Proof. It is not hard to use the above "symmetrization trick" once again in order to reduce the general case to one in which $a_n \equiv 0$ and the random variables X_i have a distribution symmetric about 0 (and hence a real characteristic function). We will take this reduction for granted, leaving the details to the reader.

Let $\phi(\lambda)$ be the (common) characteristic function of the r.v.'s X_i, and $\psi(\lambda)$ that of the limit law F. After our reduction, (1) is equivalent to

$$\lim_{n \to \infty} E\left(\exp\left[i\lambda \frac{X_1 + \cdots + X_n}{b_n}\right]\right) = \lim_{n \to \infty} \phi\left(\frac{\lambda}{b_n}\right)^n = \psi(\lambda) \quad (9)$$

for each real λ. It is evident that $\phi(\lambda/b_n) \to 1$ is necessary in order to obtain a continuous limit. This condition is automatically met if $b_n \to \infty$; otherwise, we must have $\phi(\lambda) = 1$ which corresponds to the degenerate case $X_i = 0$ a.s. that we have excluded. This proves the first assertion.

To obtain the second, suppose that there were a sequence n' such that $b_{n'+1}/b_{n'} \geq 1 + \epsilon$ for some $\epsilon > 0$. Since $b_n \to \infty$, for any $x > 0$ and $\delta > 0$ we will have

$$P\left(\frac{|X_i|}{b_n} > \frac{x\epsilon}{2}\right) \leq \delta$$

for all large enough n (and n'). Using this fact we have at continuity points

$$F(x) = \lim_{n' \to \infty} P\left(\frac{S_{n'+1}}{b_{n'+1}} \leq x\right) = \lim_{n' \to \infty} P\left(\frac{S_{n'}}{b_{n'}} \frac{b_{n'}}{b_{n'+1}} \leq x - \frac{X_{n'+1}}{b_{n'+1}}\right)$$

$$\geq \lim_{n' \to \infty} P\left(\frac{S_{n'}}{b_{n'}} \leq x(1 + \epsilon) - \frac{X_{n'+1}}{b_{n'}}\right)$$

$$\geq \lim_{n' \to \infty} P\left(\frac{S_{n'}}{b_{n'}} \leq x(1 + \epsilon) - \frac{x\epsilon}{2}\right) - \delta = F\left(x + \frac{x\epsilon}{2}\right) - \delta.$$

But since δ was arbitrary and F is nondecreasing, we have

$$F(x) = F\left(x + \frac{x\epsilon}{2}\right),$$

and this implies that F is constant on $(0, \infty)$. The same sort of argument also shows that F is constant on $(-\infty, 0)$, and hence it must be degenerate. This contradiction establishes the lemma. (Incidentally, it is true, and not much harder to prove, that $\lim (b_{n+1}/b_n) = 1$, but what we have shown will suffice for our needs.)

At last we are ready to prove Theorem 1. Choose two positive numbers α_1 and α_2; we have to show that

$$F\left(\frac{x}{\alpha_1}\right) * F\left(\frac{x}{\alpha_2}\right) = F\left(\frac{x - \beta}{\alpha_3}\right) \tag{10}$$

for some β and $\alpha_3 > 0$. Assume $\alpha_1 \geq \alpha_2$, and let $m(n)$ be an integer-valued function such that

$$\lim_{n \to \infty} \frac{b_{m(n)}}{b_n} = \frac{\alpha_1}{\alpha_2}. \tag{11}$$

Here $\{b_n\}$ is the sequence appearing in (1), and the possibility of choosing $m(n)$ to satisfy (11) is a consequence of Lemma 4.

Let us write down two special cases of (1):

$$P\left(\alpha_1 \frac{X_1 + \cdots + X_{m(n)} - a_{m(n)}}{b_{m(n)}} \leq x\right) \Rightarrow F\left(\frac{x}{\alpha_1}\right); \tag{12}$$

$$P\left(\alpha_2 \frac{X_1 + \cdots + X_n - a_n}{b_n} \leq x\right) \Rightarrow F\left(\frac{x}{\alpha_2}\right). \tag{13}$$

In view of (11), we have $\alpha_1/b_{m(n)} \sim \alpha_2/b_n$, and using Lemma 2 we see that (12) can be rewritten as

$$P\left(\alpha_2 \frac{X_1 + \cdots + X_{m(n)} - a_{m(n)}}{b_n} \leq x\right) \Rightarrow F\left(\frac{x}{\alpha_1}\right). \tag{14}$$

Now, we can convolve the distributions in (13) and (14), and by Lemma 1 the result converges to $F(x/\alpha_1) * F(x/\alpha_2)$. But convolution is equivalent to addition of independent variables so this fact implies that

$$P\left(\alpha_2 \frac{X_1 + \cdots + X_{m(n)} - a_{m(n)}}{b_n}\right.$$

$$\left. + \alpha_2 \frac{X_{m(n)+1} + \cdots + X_{m(n)+n} - a_n}{b_n} \leq x\right)$$

$$\Rightarrow F\left(\frac{x}{\alpha_1}\right) * F\left(\frac{x}{\alpha_2}\right). \tag{15}$$

But the left side is

$$P\left(\frac{\alpha_2}{b_n}\left(X_1 + \cdots + X_{m(n)+n} - a_{m(n)} - a_n\right) \le x\right),$$

which is of the same type as the distribution of $(S_{m(n)+n} - a_{m(n)+n})b_{m(n)+n}^{-1}$. Since by (1) the latter converges weakly to F, Lemma 3 assures us that the left side of (15) (which does have a nondegenerate limit) must tend to a law of the same type as F. Weak limits are unique; hence, (10) follows and the theorem is proved.

Remarks. We have shown that any limit in (1) must be stable; can the possibilities be further restricted? The answer is no, and the proof is easy:

Problem 4. If F is any stable law, show that (1) will hold for suitable constants when each X_i has F for its distribution.

The theorem we have just proved solves one problem but raises another: Under what conditions on the common law of X_i will constants exist so that (1) holds? If they do, we say that the distribution of X_i belongs to the *domain of attraction* of the stable law F, or that X_i is *attracted* by F. For example, according to Theorem 15.1 every distribution with finite variance is attracted to the normal distribution. The complete answer to this problem is known (see [GK]), but we shall be content with an example.

Problem 5. Let G be the distribution function of a measure symmetric about 0, and φ the corresponding characteristic function. Suppose that

$$\lim_{x \to +\infty} x[1 - G(x)] = c > 0. \tag{16}$$

Prove that $\varphi(\lambda) = 1 - c\pi|\lambda| + o(|\lambda|)$ as $|\lambda| \to 0$.

$\left(\textit{Hint:} \text{ write } \dfrac{1 - \varphi(\lambda)}{2\lambda} = \displaystyle\int_0^\infty \dfrac{1 - \cos \lambda x}{\lambda}\, dG(x) \text{ and break up the integral}\right.$

into several parts which can each be estimated.)

Problem 6. Show that the distribution G of Problem 5 is in the domain of attraction of the Cauchy distribution (see Problem 14.6).

In conclusion we remark that (16) is close to being necessary as well as sufficient for a symmetric law to be attracted to

Cauchy's.   The precise condition is that

$$1 - G(x) = x^{-1}L(x), \tag{17}$$

where L is a *slowly varying function* in the sense of Karamata; this means that for every constant $s > 0$,

$$\lim_{x \to \infty} \frac{L(sx)}{L(x)} = 1.$$

This class of functions plays an important role in the further study of attraction, and in many other areas of probability theory.

18. INFINITELY DIVISIBLE LAWS

Once the liberating effects of Levy's new ideas on the "central limit problem" were felt, it was inevitable that still more general questions should be asked and answered. Besides, a very familiar limit theorem—that of Poisson (see Problem 14.8)—is as yet outside the scope of our considerations. The most obvious generalization of the result of the last section is to ask for the class of possible limits in (17.1) when the X_i need no longer be identically distributed.   One caution is necessary before the problem will be meaningful: Unless we ensure that with probability approaching unity X_{n+1} is small compared to S_n, almost anything can happen.   When a condition to that effect is imposed, the problem is a good one, and has been solved.   The class of limits (called L distributions) is much larger than the stable laws, but Poisson's distribution is still not included.

It turns out to be most advantageous to generalize still further.   Instead of the members of a single sequence, let us consider (as in the beginning of Section 16) a "triangular" array of random variables $X_i^{(n)}$, $n = 1, 2, \ldots$; $i = 1, 2, \ldots, N(n)$.   For each n, $X_i^{(n)}$ are independent, and we will suppose also for the moment that they have a common distribution.   We ask: if $N(n) \to \infty$ and

$$P(X_1^{(n)} + \cdots + X_{N(n)}^{(n)} \le x) \Rightarrow F(x), \tag{1}$$

which distributions F can appear?   (The question of successive partial sums of a sequence of independent, identically distributed variables is included, for we can let $N(n) = n$ and

$X_i^{(n)} = \left(X_i - \dfrac{a_n}{n} \right) b_n^{-1}$, where the X_i, a_n and b_n are as in Section 17.) The problem as now formulated does include the Poisson theorem, for if we choose $N(n) = n$ and $X_i^{(n)} = 1$ or 0 with probabilities μ/n, $1 - \mu/n$, then (1) holds and F is the Poisson law with parameter μ. It is easy to see that this law is not stable.

A distribution F is said to be *infinitely divisible* if, for every k, F is the k-fold convolution of some distribution G_k with itself. It is equivalent to require that the characteristic function of F be the k'th power of some other characteristic function. If F is a Poisson distribution, for instance, we have

$$\phi(\lambda) = \int_{-\infty}^{\infty} e^{i\lambda x}\, dF(x) = e^{-\mu} \sum_{n=0}^{\infty} \frac{\mu^n}{n!} e^{i\lambda n} = \exp\left(\mu e^{i\lambda} - \mu \right), \quad (2)$$

which is indeed the k'th power of the Poisson characteristic function with parameter μ/k in place of μ.

Problem 1. Show that every stable law is infinitely divisible.

Problem 2. Prove that if F is infinitely divisible, so is every other distribution of the same type as F.

Problem 3. Prove that the *exponential distribution*

$$F(x) = \begin{cases} 1 - e^{-ax}, & x \geq 0, \\ 0, & x < 0, \end{cases} \quad (3)$$

where $a > 0$, is infinitely divisible, and find its "k'th root." Is it stable?

The first goal of this section is to show that the infinitely divisible laws are precisely the ones which can arise as limits in the above manner; we prove it under a slight simplifying assumption.

Theorem 1. *Suppose that* (1) *holds, where $N(n) = n$ and the $X_i^{(n)}$ are, for each n, independent with a common distribution. Then F must be infinitely divisible.*

Proof. We will show that F has a "k'th root" (with respect to convolution). Consider the subsequence $n' = m \cdot k$, and let $Y_i^{(m)} = X_{(i-1)m+1}^{(mk)} + \cdots + X_{im}^{(mk)}$.   Then

$$X_1^{(mk)} + \cdots + X_{mk}^{(mk)} = Y_1^{(m)} + \cdots + Y_k^{(m)},$$

where the Y's are independent and identically distributed (for each m), and so if

$$P(Y_1^{(m)} \le x) \Rightarrow G_k(x)$$

holds even for some subsequence of the m's, it follows by Lemma 1 of the last section that F is the k-fold convolution of G_k with itself.   Thus it is sufficient, to prove the theorem, to establish that the distributions of the $Y_i^{(m)}$ are a tight family (recall Theorem 12.3).

Suppose the contrary.   For some $\epsilon > 0$, choosing any M there is a sequence m' such that

$$P(\left| Y_1^{(m')} \right| > M) > \epsilon.$$

It is clear that there is a further subsequence such that

$$P(Y_1^{(m'')} > M) > \frac{\epsilon}{2} \qquad \text{or else} \qquad P(Y_1^{(m'')} < -M) > \frac{\epsilon}{2}$$

holds for all its members.   In the former case, say, we then have

$$P(Y_1^{(m'')} + \cdots + Y_k^{(m'')} > kM) > \left(\frac{\epsilon}{2}\right)^k,$$

so that $F(kM) \le 1 - (\epsilon/2)^k$ because of (1).   Similarly, in the latter case we get $F(-kM) \ge (\epsilon/2)^k$.   Since for each M at least one of these holds (with the same ϵ), F cannot be a distribution function.   This contradiction establishes the tightness of the laws of $Y_1^{(m)}$, and so the theorem.

Remark.   The converse—that every infinitely divisible distribution F can appear in (1) with $N(n) = n$—is immediate from the definition of an infinitely divisible law.

Two obvious problems confront us: What are the infinitely divisible laws?   Also, under what conditions does (1) hold for a given i.d. law F?   We shall aim only at giving a partial answer to the first question; the whole story may be found in [GK]. It should be remarked that the class of i.d. laws turns out to contain all possible limits for a set-up like (1) even when the variables in each row need not have a common distribution. (It is then necessary to assume that they are all small in a suitable sense.)   In particular, all L distributions are i.d.   The results in this area are remarkably general and complete.

Example. Let X_1, X_2, . . . be independent, each with characteristic function $\phi(\lambda)$, and let N have a Poisson distribution and be independent of the X_i.   The distribution of $S = X_1 + \cdots + X_N$ is said to be *compound Poisson* and is infinitely divisible as we now show:

$$E(e^{i\lambda S}) = \sum_{l=0}^{\infty} E(e^{i\lambda S}|N = l)P(N = l)$$

$$= \sum_{l=0}^{\infty} E(e^{i\lambda(X_1 + \cdots + X_l)})P(N = l) \qquad (4)$$

$$= \sum_{l=0}^{\infty} \phi(\lambda)^l \frac{e^{-\mu}\mu^l}{l!} = \exp\left[\mu\phi(\lambda) - \mu\right].$$

But on replacing μ by μ/k, the same scheme yields a characteristic function whose k'th power is $E(\exp[i\lambda S])$; hence, the latter is i.d.

It is perhaps surprising that the compound Poisson laws almost form the general case, in the following sense:

Theorem 2.   *A distribution μ is infinitely divisible if and only if it is the weak limit of a sequence of distributions, each of which is compound Poisson.*

The "if" part is an immediate consequence of the infinite divisibility of all compound Poisson laws and the following lemma.

Lemma 1.   *The weak limit of a sequence of i.d. distributions is itself i.d.*

Proof.   Let the convergent sequence be $\{\mu_n\}$, and form an array of random variables in the manner of Theorem 1; let each $X_i^{(n)}$, $i \leq n$, have as its distribution the "n'th root" of μ_n. The weak limit of the sequence becomes the distribution F of (1), and so its divisibility is established by our theorem.

Remark.   It would seem natural to use characteristic functions, and argue that if $\phi_n(\lambda) \to \phi(\lambda)$, and each ϕ_n has a k'th root which is a characteristic function, these roots must converge to a function which provides the desired k'th root of ϕ. This argument can be justified, but a little more care is needed than may be evident at first sight in order to show the convergence of the roots of ϕ.

Lemma 2. *The characteristic function of an i.d. law never vanishes.*

Proof. For any real characteristic function $\psi(\lambda)$, corresponding to some (symmetric) distribution G, we have

$$1 - \psi(2\lambda) \leq 4[1 - \psi(\lambda)]. \tag{5}$$

This fact is easy to prove:

$$1 - \psi(2\lambda) = \int_{-\infty}^{\infty} (1 - \cos 2x\lambda) \, dG(x) = 2 \int_{-\infty}^{\infty} \sin^2 \lambda x \, dG(x)$$

$$= 2 \int_{-\infty}^{\infty} (1 - \cos \lambda x)(1 + \cos \lambda x) \, dG(x)$$

$$\leq 4 \int_{-\infty}^{\infty} (1 - \cos \lambda x) \, dG(x) = 4[1 - \phi(\lambda)].$$

Now, let ϕ be the i.d. characteristic function in question. We can assume it is real, for in any case $|\phi(\lambda)|^2$ is again an i.d. characteristic function, and has the same zeros as ϕ. Let ϕ_k denote that k'th root of ϕ which is a characteristic function, and note that there is some interval $[a, a]$ where $\phi(\lambda) > 0$, and hence on which $\phi_k(\lambda) \to 1$ uniformly as $k \to \infty$. According to (5), if $[1 - \phi_k(\lambda)] < 1/4$ in $[-a, a]$ then $[1 - \phi_k(\lambda)] < 1$ in the larger interval $[-2a, 2a]$. Iterating (5), we obtain

$$1 - \phi_k(2^m\lambda) \leq 4^m[1 - \phi_k(\lambda)].$$

If we choose k to make the right side less than 1 in $[-a, a]$, as we can, it follows that ϕ_k (and so also ϕ) does not vanish in $[-2^m a, 2^m a]$. As $a > 0$ and m is arbitrary, this accomplishes the proof of Lemma 2.

Lemma 3. *For each k, let ϕ_k be a characteristic function whose k'th power is ϕ. Then*

$$\lim_{k \to \infty} \phi_k(\lambda) = 1 \qquad \text{for all real } \lambda. \tag{6}$$

Proof. Since $\phi(\lambda)$ is continuous and never vanishes, there is a unique way to define the function arg $\phi(\lambda)$ which is continuous and makes arg $\phi(0) = 0$.[9]   Similarly, there is a unique definition of arg $\phi_k(\lambda)$ meeting the same requirements; in fact,

$$\text{arg } \phi_k(\lambda) = \frac{\text{arg } \phi(\lambda)}{k} \tag{7}$$

is the only choice.   To see this, observe that because $\phi_k(\lambda)^k = \phi(\lambda)$, the possibilities for arg $\phi_k(\lambda)$ are

$$\frac{\text{arg } \phi(\lambda)}{k} + j\frac{2\pi}{k}, \qquad j = 0, 1, \ldots, k - 1.$$

At $\lambda = 0$, the choice $j = 0$ is required, and since arg $\phi(\lambda)$ is continuous, if any value of $j \neq 0$ is ever used arg $\phi_k(\lambda)$ will have a discontinuity.   But from (7), and the fact that

$$\left|\phi_k(\lambda)\right| = \left|\phi(\lambda)\right|^{1/k} \to 1$$

for each λ, the assertion (6) of Lemma 3 is obvious.

   Now for the "only if" part of the theorem.   We will use logarithms of our characteristic functions; these are defined using that version of "arg ϕ" discussed in the last paragraph. Let ϕ be the characteristic function of the i.d. distribution μ, and ϕ_k its "k'th root" as before.   We have

$$\log \phi(\lambda) = k \log \phi_k(\lambda),$$

and because of Lemma 3 we can write

$$\log \phi(\lambda) = \lim_{k \to \infty} k[\phi_k(\lambda) - 1]. \tag{8}$$

But (8) is equivalent to

$$\phi(\lambda) = \lim_{k \to \infty} \exp\left[k\left(\phi_k(\lambda) - 1\right)\right], \tag{9}$$

and the exponential on the right is a compound Poisson characteristic function for each k.   In view of Theorem 14.2 the corresponding distributions converge weakly to μ, and so Theorem 2 is proved.

   Problem 4.   Exhibit a sequence of compound Poisson laws which converge to the normal distribution, and prove that it is not itself compound Poisson.

   [9] This point (which has nothing to do with probability as such) is a little trickier than it may appear.   The reader not familiar with such matters will do well to think through the construction.

Much more specific results than Theorem 2 are known. Kolmogorov proved that any i.d. distribution with finite variance has a characteristic function representable in the form

$$\phi(\lambda) = \exp\left[i\lambda m + \int_{-\infty}^{\infty} \frac{e^{i\lambda x} - 1 - i\lambda x}{x^2} \, dG(x)\right], \quad (10)$$

where G is an increasing function of bounded variation. Somewhat later, Khintchine and Levy found similar representations which are valid with no restrictions. We will conclude this section with four problems which outline the derivation of (10).

Problem 5.   If ϕ is the characteristic function of an i.d. law F with mean m, then show that

$$\log \phi(\lambda) = im\lambda + \lim_{k \to \infty} \int_{-\infty}^{\infty} (e^{i\lambda x} - 1 - i\lambda x)k \, dF_k(x), \quad (11)$$

where F_k is the distribution whose k-fold convolution is F.

Problem 6.   If F has finite variance σ^2, prove that the monotonic functions

$$G_k(x) = k \int_{-\infty}^{x} u^2 \, dF_k(u) \quad (12)$$

are uniformly bounded, and so that there is a subsequence of $\{G_k\}$ whose corresponding measures are weakly convergent when restricted to any compact interval.

Problem 7.   For the subsequence of the last problem, show that

$$\lim_{k \to \infty} \int_{-\infty}^{\infty} \frac{e^{i\lambda x} - 1 - i\lambda x}{x^2} \, dG_k(x) = \int_{-\infty}^{\infty} \frac{e^{i\lambda x} - 1 - i\lambda x}{x^2} \, dG(x), \quad (13)$$

where G is increasing and of total variation at most σ^2.   Relations (13) and (11) combined establish Kolmogorov's formula (10).

Problem 8.   Show that every function of the form (10) is an infinitely divisible characteristic function.   (*Hint:* Use Theorem 2.)

19.   RECURRENCE

We have made a survey of the theory of limiting distributions for sums of independent random variables; in the main, these problems were rather completely solved during the 1930's and early 1940's.   This theory does not, however, contain everything worth knowing about sums of independent variables! We have already, in Chapter 2, considered several properties of the sequence $\{S_n\}$ of partial sums which hold (or fail) almost surely; in this section we study one more problem of that sort. The variables will always be assumed to have a common distribution.

A *simple random walk* in d dimensions means the partial sums S_n of a sequence of independent r.v.'s, each of which takes as its values the unit vectors along one of the coordinate axes ($+$ or $-$ direction) with every choice having equal probability $1/2d$. We know from Section 9 that

$$P(|S_n| = O(\sqrt{n \log \log n})) = 1,\text{[10]} \tag{1}$$

but it is not clear whether or not $S_n = 0$ (or some other fixed possible value) occurs repeatedly or not. This question was first raised and answered by George Polya as long ago as 1921; the result is that if $d = 1$ or 2, $S_n = 0$ occurs infinitely often with probability 1, while when $d > 2$ the probability is zero. (See [F].) It is curious that Polya's interesting discovery was not suitably generalized until 1951, when K. L. Chung and W. H. J. Fuchs gave a nice treatment for general independent, identically-distributed random vectors. We will discuss here only the one-dimensional case, and follow Chung and Fuchs by using characteristic functions although other methods of attack are now known.

It simplifies the problem technically to assume that the r.v.'s X_i take on only integer values (a.s.), and we will do so. In this case we say that the sequence $\{S_n\}$ of sums is *recurrent* if

$$P(S_n = 0 \text{ infinitely often}) = 1; \tag{2}$$

it is *transient* otherwise. (The probability is then 0, as we will soon see.) It is clear that (2) could never occur if X_i had a continuous distribution, and so in the general case we speak instead of *interval recurrence*, meaning that S_n almost surely returns to a neighborhood of 0 rather than to 0 itself. With this change, the results in general are much the same as in the special case of integer-valued variables.

---

[10] If $d > 1$, the one-dimensional result still holds for each coordinate.

We may start by noting one fact which is immediate from previous results: *if $E(X_i)$ exists, and is not equal to 0, then $\{S_n\}$ is transient.* This follows from the strong law of large numbers (Theorem 8.1), since lim $S_n/n = \mu \neq 0$ then holds a.s. and is not compatible with recurrence. We shall see later that when $\mu = 0$ the sequence $\{S_n\}$ *is recurrent*; note that this statement does not at all follow from the law of large numbers, or even from stronger estimates like (1).

Remark. There is an exception to this statement. When $d = 1$, the full law of the iterated logarithm (if it applies) shows that $S_n > 0$ and $S_n < 0$ both occur infinitely often. If the only positive (or negative) value X_i can take is $+1$ (-1), then each passage from negative to positive ($+$ to $-$) states must contain a zero. In this special case, therefore, previous results do imply recurrence.

Lemma 1. *The probability that infinitely many of the events $\{S_n = 0\}$ occur is 1 or 0, according as $\sum_n P(S_n = 0)$ diverges or converges.*

Proof. It is immediate from the Borel-Cantelli lemma that if $\Sigma P(S_n = 0) < \infty$, then $S_n = 0$ occurs at most finitely often a.s. The converse part of that lemma does not apply since the events $\{S_n = 0\}$ are not independent, but we will show that the conclusion it would yield holds anyway. The proof exploits the fact that the "shifted" sequence of sums X_k, $X_k + X_{k+1}$, . . . has exactly the same probabilistic properties as the original sequence $\{S_n\}$.

Clearly, we can write

$$1 \geq P(S_n = 0 \text{ finitely often})$$
$$= \sum_{n=1}^{\infty} P(S_n = 0, S_m \neq 0 \text{ for } m > n), \quad (3)$$

since if there are only finitely many $S_n = 0$ there must be a last one. But using independence and the idea mentioned above,

$$P(S_n = 0, S_m \neq 0 \text{ for } m > n)$$
$$= P(S_n = 0)P(S_m - S_n \neq 0 \text{ for } m > n) \quad (4)$$
$$= P(S_n = 0)P(S_m \neq 0 \text{ for all } m \geq 1).$$

Combining (3) and (4), we have

$$1 \geq \sum_{n=1}^{\infty} P(S_n = 0)P(S_m \neq 0 \text{ for all } m \geq 1),$$

and since we are assuming that $\Sigma P(S_n = 0)$ diverges the last factor must vanish, so that

$$P(S_m = 0 \text{ for some } m \geq 1) = 1. \tag{5}$$

It is easy to prove by induction that the probability of at least k "visits to 0" is also one for every k. Supposing this known for $k - 1$, we can write

$$P(S_n = 0 \text{ at least } k \text{ times})$$
$$= \sum_{n=1}^{\infty} P(S_i \neq 0 \text{ for } i < n,$$
$$S_n = 0, S_m - S_n = 0 \text{ for at least } k - 1 \text{ values } m > n)$$
$$= \sum_{n=1}^{\infty} P(S_i \neq 0 \text{ for } i < n, S_n = 0)$$
$$P(S_m = 0 \text{ at least } k - 1 \text{ times}).$$

By (5) and the induction hypothesis the last expression is one, so for every k there are a.s. k visits to 0. It is an evident consequence that $\{S_n\}$ is recurrent, and the lemma is proved.

Remark. For the reader familiar with "recurrent events" or Markov chains (see [F]), this lemma is immediate. Indeed, $\{S_n\}$ forms a denumerable Markov chain, and it is always true that the number of times the initial state is visited in such a chain is a.s. infinite if its expectation (in our case $\Sigma P(S_n = 0)$) diverges.

Let $\phi(\lambda)$ be the common characteristic function of the r.v.'s X_i; then

$$\phi(\lambda)^n = E(e^{i\lambda S_n}) = \sum_{k=-\infty}^{\infty} e^{i\lambda k} P(S_n = k). \tag{6}$$

This is, of course, a Fourier series, and so the "inversion formula" we need is just

$$P(S_n = 0) = \frac{1}{2\pi} \int_{-\pi}^{\pi} \phi(\lambda)^n \, d\lambda. \tag{7}$$

It is tempting to sum under the integral sign in (7), but some care is needed. It is easy, however, to justify the following:

$$\sum_{n=0}^{\infty} P(S_n = 0)x^n = \frac{1}{2\pi} \int_{-\pi}^{\pi} \frac{1}{1 - x\phi(\lambda)} \, d\lambda \qquad \text{for } |x| < 1. \quad (8)$$

Combining (8) with the lemma above yields the following result:

Theorem 1. $\{S_n\}$ *is recurrent or transient according to whether*

$$\lim_{x \to 1-} \frac{1}{2\pi} \int_{-\pi}^{\pi} \frac{d\lambda}{1 - x\phi(\lambda)} \quad (9)$$

is infinite or finite.

We will use this result to establish the fact mentioned above:

Theorem 2. *If $E(X_i)$ exists and equals 0, $\{S_n\}$ is recurrent.*

Proof. As shown in the lemma near the beginning of Section 15, $\phi'(\lambda)$ exists and is continuous, and $\phi'(0) = iE(X_i) = 0$. Hence, we can write

$$\phi(\lambda) = 1 - o(|\lambda|) \quad (10)$$

for λ near 0. It is possible, in other words, for any $\epsilon > 0$ to choose $\delta > 0$ so that

$$|1 - \phi(\lambda)| \le \epsilon|\lambda| \qquad \text{for } |\lambda| \le \delta. \quad (11)$$

The quantity $1 - \phi(\lambda)$ need not be real, of course, but (11) implies that both its real and imaginary parts are at most $\epsilon|\lambda|$ in the neighborhood we have chosen.

To use this fact, we will write, for $x \in (0, 1)$,

$$\begin{aligned}
\int_{-\pi}^{\pi} \frac{d\lambda}{1 - x\phi(\lambda)} &= \int_{-\pi}^{\pi} \text{Re}\left[\frac{1}{1 - x\phi(\lambda)}\right] d\lambda \\
&\ge \int_{-\delta}^{\delta} \text{Re}\left[\frac{1}{1 - x\phi(\lambda)}\right] d\lambda \quad (12) \\
&= \int_{-\delta}^{\delta} \frac{1 - x\,\text{Re}\,[\phi(\lambda)]}{|1 - x\phi(\lambda)|^2} \, d\lambda.
\end{aligned}$$

Expanding and using (11) it is easy to see that when $|\lambda| \le \delta$

$$|1 - x\phi(\lambda)|^2 \le (1 - x + x\epsilon|\lambda|)^2 + x^2\epsilon^2|\lambda|^2$$
$$\le 2(1 - x)^2 + 3x^2\epsilon^2\lambda^2$$
$$\le 3[(1 - x)^2 + \epsilon^2\lambda^2]. \quad (13)$$

Combining (12) and (13), we obtain

$$\int_{-\pi}^{\pi} \frac{d\lambda}{1 - x\phi(\lambda)} \ge \frac{1}{3} \int_{-\delta}^{\delta} \frac{1 - x}{(1 - x)^2 + \epsilon^2\lambda^2} \, d\lambda = \frac{2}{3\epsilon} \tan^{-1} \frac{\delta\epsilon}{1 - x}.$$

As a result it is obvious that

$$\lim_{x \to 1-} \inf \int_{-\pi}^{\pi} \frac{d\lambda}{1 - x\phi(\lambda)} \ge \frac{\pi}{3\epsilon}, \quad (14)$$

and since ϵ was arbitrary (> 0) the limit in (9) must be infinite. Hence, according to Theorem 1, $\{S_n\}$ is recurrent.

It is not by any means necessary for recurrence that the expectation should exist. By methods rather similar to the above, again using Theorem 1, it is not too hard to give examples:

Problem 1. Suppose that the common distribution of the variables X_n is symmetric about 0, concentrated on integers, and satisfies condition (16) of Problem 17.5. Then $E(X_n)$ does not exist, and the weak law of large numbers does not hold, but $\{S_n\}$ is nevertheless recurrent. (*Hint:* Use the result established in that problem.)

In conclusion, we will state some of the facts in higher dimensions. In the plane, first moment zero is no longer sufficient for recurrence, but finite variances are enough. (Of course, the mean must be 0, or transience will again follow from the strong law of large numbers.) If, however, the dimension is three or more—and if there is no two-dimensional subspace in which X_n lies a.s.—then recurrence can never occur. These results (due to Chung and Fuchs) can also be proved fairly directly by Fourier-analytic methods. Details can be found in their paper [4], or in the book [S] by F. Spitzer which provides an excellent exposition of recent work on sums of independent random variables. The central limit problem is not included in [S], being well treated elsewhere. Instead the book treats other properties of which recurrence is one of the simplest, and describes a fascinating theory of quite a different sort. We will not go farther into the subject here.

4

Stochastic Processes

20. BROWNIAN MOTION—INTRODUCTION

Under certain conditions, small particles suspended in a fluid can be observed to undergo a continual, irregular motion. This phenomenon is named after its 19th century discoverer, Robert Brown. Its explanation lies in the fact that the particle suffers innumerable collisions with the "randomly" moving molecules of the surrounding fluid; each collision has individually a negligible effect but cumulatively they produce the observable motion.

A mathematical theory for Brownian motion was put forward at the beginning of this century by Bachelier and Einstein. Let x_t denote one coordinate of the Brownian particle at time t, where for reference we take $x_0 = 0$. Since the underlying molecular motions can be known only statistically, x_t will be a random variable. As the displacement during the period $[0, t]$ is the sum of many very small, almost independent contributions, it is plausible in view of the central limit theorem to postulate that x_t is normally distributed. Relatively high viscosity is assumed, so that the velocity of the particle is very quickly damped out; as a result, the displacements undergone in nonoverlapping intervals of time should be independent. By symmetry, $E(x_t) = 0$, and if the physical conditions remain constant we should have $E[(x_{t+s} - x_t)^2] = f(s)$ independent of t. This latter condition, with the assumed independence, leads to the choice $f(s) = cs$ for the variance.[1]

These considerations already form an experimentally testable theory, but mathematically they are certainly less than satisfactory. Complete sense was made of them for the first time by Norbert Wiener in 1923. Let us define a *standard Brownian motion process* (or *Wiener process*) as follows: Upon some probability space $(\Omega, \mathcal{B}, P)$, there is defined a family $\{x_t, t \geq 0\}$ of random variables satisfying

   (i) $x_0(\omega) = 0$ a.s.
   (ii) If $0 = t_0 < t_1 < \cdots < t_n$, then the random variables $x_{t_{i+1}} - x_{t_i}$, $i = 0, 1, \ldots, n - 1$, are independent.
   (iii) For each s, $t \geq 0$, $x_{t+s} - x_t$ is normally distributed with mean 0 and variance cs.
   (iv) For almost all $\omega \in \Omega$, the function $x_t = x_t(\omega)$ is everywhere continuous in t.[2]

Such a process would seem to fulfill the above desiderata for a model of (physical) Brownian motion, but its existence is not at all obvious.

There are two basically different approaches to the construction of a Wiener process. The simpler, but less general, method is to represent the functions x_t by some set of parameters, such as Fourier coefficients, which can be taken to be independent random variables. This was Wiener's approach; we shall present in detail below a modified version of it, due to Ciesielski and Kampé de Feriet, which is technically simpler to handle. The other method will be discussed later, and used to construct many *stochastic processes* besides Wiener's.

Let us first give some heuristics. Suppose that $x_t(\omega)$ is a Wiener process, $0 \leq t \leq 1$, and let $\{\psi_n(t)\}$ be any complete orthonormal system of functions in $L_2[0, 1]$. If a representa-

[1] The constant c is important for the physical theory. Einstein derived a relation between c, some measurable parameters of the system, and Avogadro's number, which led to an accurate method of measuring the latter by observing particles undergoing Brownian motion.

[2] It is intended to represent the motion in time of a physical particle.

tion of x_t in the form

$$x_t(\omega) = \sum_{n=1}^{\infty} a_n(\omega) \psi_n(t) \tag{1}$$

is to be possible, the coefficients "should" be given by the formula

$$a_n(\omega) = \int_0^1 x_\tau(\omega) \psi_n(\tau) \, d\tau. \tag{2}$$

Since a_n is a sort of linear combination of normally-distributed r.v.'s, we expect that it will itself be normal; taking the operation "E" under the integral sign we have $E(a_n) = 0$. It would be most pleasant, as hinted above, if $\{a_n\}$ were independent; for this, it is at least necessary that $E(a_n a_m) = 0$ when $n \neq m$.[3] Can this be achieved by a proper choice of $\{\psi_n(t)\}$?

There is a unique basis $\{\psi_n\}$ which will work. Formally, at least, we can write

$$E(a_n a_m) = \int_0^1 \int_0^1 E(x_t x_s) \psi_n(t) \psi_m(s) \, dt \, ds. \tag{3}$$

The function $E(x_t x_s)$ is easily found from our assumptions. Take $t < s$; then

$$E(x_t x_s) = E(x_t[x_t + (x_s - x_t)]) = E(x_t^2) + 0 = ct, \tag{4}$$

because of postulates (i), (ii), and (iii). For convenience we will take $c = 1$ from now on. Hence,

$$E(x_t x_s) = \min(s, t), \tag{5}$$

which is continuous and positive definite. From these facts, it is not hard to see that $\{\psi_n\}$ must be the (normalized) *eigenfunctions* of the kernel given in (5), and these are just the functions $\{\sin(n + \frac{1}{2})\pi t\}$. Thus, if the coefficients a_n are to be independent, (1) *must* be a type of classical Fourier series.

Problem 1. Verify the assertions of the sentence before the last one above.

To complete Wiener's approach, we must reverse the above steps; starting with the proper basis and coefficients $\{a_n(\omega)\}$ which are independent normal r.v.'s with the right variances (easily computed), we wish to show that (1) converges to a con-

---

[3] Since it turns out that the $\{a_n\}$ must have a joint normal distribution, this condition is also sufficient. We will not discuss multivariate normal laws in this book; although some knowledge of them would be convenient at present, it is not indispensable.

tinuous function for almost all ω. This is not easy, and we will not do it.[4] Instead we look for a slightly different approach, in which we are free to use another basis more convenient to handle. We wish to keep the independence of the coefficients $\{a_n\}$, and so the functions replacing $\{\psi_n\}$ can no longer be orthogonal.

Such an approach can be based on the derivative of the Wiener process. (This derivative really exists only in the generalized-function (Schwartz distribution) sense, but we are, for now, ignoring questions of rigor.) It is plausible that if x_t *were* differentiable, $(dx/dt) = x_t'$ would be normally distributed, and that x_t' and x_s' would be independent for $t \neq s$ because of postulate (ii). Moreover, we "should" have

$$E(x_t' x_s') = \delta(t - s), \tag{6}$$

where δ is the "Dirac delta function."

Problem 2. Give a heuristic argument leading to the above "results" about the "process" $\{x_t'\}$.

Let us apply to $\{x_t'\}$ the arguments we developed above for $\{x_t\}$ itself. In order to have an orthogonal expansion of the form (1), we saw that it is necessary for the basis $\{\psi_n(t)\}$ to consist of eigenfunctions of the kernel $E(x_s x_t)$. When this kernel is a continuous function the basis is thereby determined almost uniquely. However, for the kernel (6) of $\{x_t'\}$, any complete orthonormal set will do! (Any function is an eigenfunction of $\delta(t - s)$.) Hence, we have formally

$$x_t'(\omega) = \sum_{n=1}^{\infty} a_n(\omega)\psi_n(t) \tag{7}$$

for any basis $\{\psi_n\}$ of $L_2[0, 1]$. The coefficients a_n are normal, independent r.v.'s with mean 0, and their variance is 1:

$$\begin{aligned}
E(a_n{}^2) &= E\left\{\int_0^1 \int_0^1 x_t' x_s' \psi_n(t)\psi_n(s)\, dt\, ds\right\} \\
&= \int_0^1 \int_0^1 \delta(t - s)\psi_n(t)\psi_n(s)\, dt\, ds \\
&= \int_0^1 \psi_n{}^2(s)\, ds = 1. \quad (8)
\end{aligned}$$

[4] Nor did Wiener do quite that; he proved almost sure uniform convergence for (1) with the terms grouped into blocks in a special way.

Of course, the series (7) with coefficients chosen as above does not converge. But we sought a development, not of x'_t, but of x_t, and so we are led to consider

$$x_t(\omega) = \sum_{n=1}^{\infty} a_n(\omega) \int_0^t \psi_n(\tau) \, d\tau \tag{9}$$

where $\{\psi_n\}$ can be any complete, orthonormal set in $L_2[0, 1]$, and a_n are independent normal r.v.'s with mean 0 and unit variance. Since $\int_0^t \psi_n(\tau) \, d\tau$ is continuous, the a.s. uniform convergence of (9) would yield a process satisfying postulate (iv), and also the others if our formal considerations have not led us astray. It has recently been proved by M. Nisio that the series in (9) is in fact a.s. uniformly convergent, regardless of what basis is used. This elegant theorem requires some advanced tools for its proof, but a special case can be established very simply, and, of course, is enough to show the existence of Wiener's process satisfying (i) to (iv). This special case is the method mentioned above; we will present it in the next section.

21. THE FIRST CONSTRUCTION

We choose, as the orthonormal sequence $\{\psi_n(t)\}$, the *Haar functions*. These functions have some very nice properties, so that the proof that (20.9) converges will be quite easy. They are defined as follows:

$$H_0(t) = 1, \, 0 \le t \le 1; \qquad H_1(t) = \begin{cases} +1, & 0 \le t \le \frac{1}{2}, \\ -1, & \frac{1}{2} < t \le 1; \end{cases} \tag{1}$$

and in general, for $2^n \le k < 2^{n+1}$, we set

$$H_k(t) = \begin{cases} 2^{n/2} & \text{for } \dfrac{k - 2^n}{2^n} \le t \le \dfrac{k - 2^n + (1/2)}{2^n}, \\[2mm] -2^{n/2} & \text{for } \dfrac{k - 2^n + (1/2)}{2^n} < t \le \dfrac{k - 2^n + 1}{2^n}, \\[2mm] 0, & \text{otherwise.} \end{cases} \tag{2}$$

It is easy to check that these functions are indeed orthonormal. They are also complete; in fact, they have the property that the (generalized) Fourier expansion of any continuous function converges uniformly to the function. However, we will make use of completeness only in the form of Parseval's relation

$$(f, g) = \sum_{k=0}^{\infty} (f, H_k)(g, H_k). \tag{3}$$

Here, f and g are real, square-integrable functions on $[0, 1]$ and parentheses denote the L_2 inner product

$$(f, g) = \int_0^1 f(t)g(t) \, dt. \tag{4}$$

We will not prove (3) here; see, for instance, [KS].

The special feature that makes the Haar functions convenient for us is the following:

Lemma 1. *The series*

$$\sum_{k=0}^{\infty} a_k \int_0^t H_k(\tau) \, d\tau = s(t) \tag{5}$$

is uniformly convergent provided that $|a_k| = O(k^\epsilon)$ *for some* $\epsilon < (1/2)$.

Proof. It is very easy to see that the functions[5] $S_k(t) = \int_0^t H_k(\tau) \, d\tau$ are nonnegative and attain a maximum value of $2^{-n/2}/4$ provided $2^n \leq k < 2^{n+1}$. Furthermore, as k varies over this range the functions S_k have disjoint supports. Hence, writing

$$b_n = \max_{2^n \leq k < 2^{n+1}} |a_k|, \tag{6}$$

it is almost immediate, using Cauchy's criterion, that

$$\sum_{n=0}^{\infty} b_n 2^{-n/2} < \infty \tag{7}$$

is sufficient for the uniform absolute convergence of (5). If the condition of the lemma is met, we have $|b_n| < C2^{\epsilon n}$, and so (7) certainly holds.

We actually wish to choose $\{a_k\}$ to be a sequence of independent, normal r.v.'s with mean 0, variance 1. Such a sequence must, with probability 1, satisfy the conditions of Lemma 1 with a good deal to spare:

[5] The $S_k(t)$ are called "Schauder functions."

Lemma 2.   *If $\{X_n\}$ are normal r.v.'s with mean 0 and variance 1, then*

$$P(|X_n| = O(\sqrt{\log n})) = 1. \tag{8}$$

Proof.   This is just the estimate which follows from the easy part of the Borel-Cantelli lemma; that is why independence plays no role.   (In the independent case, the accuracy of the bound can be tested using the second part of the B.-C. lemma.)

We need a simple estimate which is easily derived by an integration by parts.   For $x > 0$,

$$P(|X_n| \geq x) = \frac{2}{\sqrt{2\pi}} \int_x^\infty e^{-u^2/2} \, du$$

$$= \frac{2}{\sqrt{2\pi}} \left\{ \frac{e^{-x^2/2}}{x} - \int_x^\infty \frac{e^{-u^2/2}}{u^2} \, du \right\}.$$

Since, for large x, the second term in the braces is clearly of smaller order of magnitude than the integral we wish to estimate, it is evident that

$$P(|X_n| \geq x) \sim \sqrt{\frac{2}{\pi}} \frac{e^{-x^2/2}}{x} \tag{9}$$

as $x \to \infty$.   Using (9), we have

$$\sum_{n=2}^\infty P(|X_n| \geq c \sqrt{\log n}) \leq K \sum_{n=2}^\infty \frac{n^{-c^2/2}}{\sqrt{\log n}}, \tag{10}$$

and so if $c > \sqrt{2}$ the left-hand side is finite.   This is sufficient to prove (8).

We are now ready for the main result:

Theorem 1.   *Let $\{X_n\}$ be a sequence of independent r.v.'s each normally distributed with mean 0 and variance 1.   With probability one, the series*

$$\sum_{n=0}^\infty X_n(\omega) \int_0^t H_n(\tau) \, d\tau = x_t(\omega) \tag{11}$$

is uniformly convergent, and the random variables $\{x_t, 0 \leq t \leq 1\}$ which it determines form a Brownian motion process in the sense of Section 20.

Proof. The (almost sure) uniform convergence of (11) is immediate from Lemmas 1 and 2 above, and since the functions $\int_0^t H_n(\tau)\, d\tau$ are each continuous in t and vanish at $t = 0$, the sum x_t must have these properties also. Thus only properties (ii) and (iii) of the definition—asserting that $\{x_t\}$ has *independent increments* which are normally distributed—remain to be proved.

So far we have used neither the independence of the $\{X_i\}$ nor the completeness of the Haar functions; both will be required soon. The proof will proceed by showing that for each k

$$E\left\{\exp\left[i\sum_{j=1}^{k} \lambda_j(x_{t_j} - x_{t_{j-1}})\right]\right\}$$

$$= \prod_{j=1}^{k} \exp\left\{-\frac{1}{2}(t_j - t_{j-1})^2\lambda_j^2\right\}, \quad (12)$$

where $0 = t_0 < t_1 < \cdots < t_k$ and $\lambda_1, \ldots, \lambda_k$ are any real numbers. The left side of (12) is the *joint characteristic function* of the random variables $(x_{t_j} - x_{t_{j-1}})$. The right side is clearly (recall (14.7)) what should be obtained if these variables are independent and normally distributed with mean 0 and variances $t_j - t_{j-1}$; in other words, if (ii) and (iii) of the definition of Brownian motion do hold as we have asserted. When (12) is established, then, the proof that (11) is a Brownian motion will be complete, provided the joint characteristic function (like its one-dimensional counterpart) determines uniquely the probability measure on R^k from which it was obtained. We will discuss that point at the end of this section.

Turning to the derivation of (12), we assume for simplicity that $k = 2$. We then have, using (11),

$$E(\exp[i\lambda_1 x_{t_1} + i\lambda_2(x_{t_2} - x_{t_1})]) = E(\exp[i(\lambda_1 - \lambda_2)x_{t_1} + i\lambda_2 x_{t_2}])$$

$$= E\left(\exp\sum_{n=0}^{\infty} X_n[i(\lambda_1 - \lambda_2)S_n(t_1) + i\lambda_2 S_n(t_2)]\right). \quad (13)$$

But since the X_n are independent the last expression factors (recall Corollary 10.4); each term is simply the characteristic function of a single X_n evaluated at a suitable point. In this way (13) becomes

$$\prod_{n=0}^{\infty} \exp\left\{-\frac{1}{2}[(\lambda_1 - \lambda_2)S_n(t_1) + \lambda_2 S_n(t_2)]^2\right\}$$

$$= \exp\left\{-\frac{1}{2}\sum_{n=0}^{\infty}[(\lambda_1 - \lambda_2)^2 S_n(t_1)^2 + 2(\lambda_1 - \lambda_2)\lambda_2 S_n(t_1)S_n(t_2)\right.$$

$$\left. + \lambda_2^2 S_n(t_2)^2]\right\}. \quad (14)$$

The sums are easily evaluated, using Parseval's relation (3) for the Haar functions. Indeed, if

$$\phi_s(\tau) = \begin{cases} 1 & \text{if } 0 \le \tau \le s, \\ 0 & \text{if } s < \tau \le 1, \end{cases}$$

then for any $s_1 \le s_2$ in $[0, 1]$ we have by (3)

$$s_1 = (\phi_{s_1}, \phi_{s_2}) = \sum_{n=0}^{\infty} (\phi_{s_1}, H_n)(\phi_{s_2}, H_n)$$

$$= \sum_{n=0}^{\infty} S_n(s_1)S_n(s_2). \quad (15)$$

With the aid of (15), (14) can be rewritten as

$$\exp\left\{-\tfrac{1}{2}[(\lambda_1 - \lambda_2)^2 t_1 + 2(\lambda_1 - \lambda_2)\lambda_2 t_1 + \lambda_2^2 t_2]\right\}$$
$$= \exp\left\{-\tfrac{1}{2}[t_1\lambda_1^2 + (t_2 - t_1)\lambda_2^2]\right\},$$

which is the right side of (12). Thus (12) is established for $k = 2$ or for $k = 1$ (putting $\lambda_2 = 0$).

Problem 1. Generalize the argument above to prove (12) for any value of k.

We have now shown that Brownian motion on the time interval $[0, 1]$ exists; how about $[0, \infty)$? Notice that the measure-theoretic part of our construction is completely contained in the sentence "Let $\{X_n\}$ be a sequence of independent r.v.'s . . . ." If such a sequence exists (recall Section 4) it is clearly possible by renumbering to produce a countable number of similar sequences, all independent of each other. These sequences can be used, via (11), to produce a sequence of independent random functions $\{x_t^{(n)}(\omega)\}$, $0 \leq t \leq 1$.   Finally we can piece these functions together: Define $x_t(\omega) = x_t^{(1)}(\omega)$ for $0 \leq t \leq 1$, and proceeding inductively put

$$x_t(\omega) = x_{t-n+1}^{(n)}(\omega) + x_{n-1}(\omega) \qquad \text{for } n - 1 \leq t \leq n. \quad (16)$$

This determines a continuous function (a.s.) for all $0 \leq t < \infty$.

Problem 2.   Show that $\{x_t(\omega)\}$, defined by (16) above, is a Brownian motion process on the time-interval $[0, \infty)$.

Finally, the matter of the uniqueness theorem for joint characteristic functions must be dealt with.   Its use, of course, goes far beyond the present situation.

Proposition. *Let P be any Borel probability measure on R^n, and define its characteristic function by*

$$\phi(\lambda_1, \ldots, \lambda_n) = \int_{R^n} \exp\left\{i \sum_{j=1}^n \lambda_j x_j\right\} dP(x_1, \ldots, x_n). \quad (17)$$

Then the function ϕ uniquely determines the measure P.

Sketch of Proof.   We can imitate the proof of Theorem 14.1 quite closely.   Define a *normal distribution* on R^n by means of the density function

$$f(x_1, \ldots, x_n) = \frac{1}{(\sqrt{2\pi}\,\sigma)^n} \exp\left\{-\frac{1}{2\sigma^2} \sum_{j=1}^n x_j^2\right\}, \quad (18)$$

and let P_σ be the measure obtained by convolving P with the normal distribution (18).   The operation of convolution, just as in one dimension, corresponds to the addition of independent random vectors, and has the effect of multiplying the corresponding characteristic functions.   Proceeding in complete analogy with the method used in Section 14, we find that P_σ has a density f_σ given by

$$f_\sigma(x_1, \ldots, x_n) = \frac{1}{(2\pi)^n} \int_{R^n} \exp\left\{-i \sum_{j=1}^n \lambda_j x_j\right\} \phi_\sigma(\lambda)\, d\lambda. \quad (19)$$

Here, $\lambda = (\lambda_1, \ldots, \lambda_n)$, $d\lambda$ means Lebesgue measure on R^n, and

$$\phi_\sigma(\lambda) = \exp\left\{-\frac{\sigma^2}{2}\sum_{j=1}^{n}\lambda_j{}^2\right\}\phi(\lambda) \tag{20}$$

is the characteristic function of P_σ. Thus P_σ is uniquely determined by ϕ for each $\sigma > 0$. But it is not hard to show that for each continuous function g on R^n with compact support,

$$\lim_{\sigma\to 0}\int_{R^n} g\,dP_\sigma = \int_{R^n} g\,dP, \tag{21}$$

so that the P integral of g is also determined by ϕ. It follows easily that P is itself determined; this proves the proposition and also completes the proof of Theorem 1.

    Problem 3.   Prove (21).

    Problem 4.   Prove that two Borel probability measures P and P' on R^n, such that

$$\int_{R^n} g\,dP = \int_{R^n} g\,dP'$$

for each continuous g with compact support, must be identical.

22. SOME PROPERTIES OF BROWNIAN PATHS

    This section will discuss some qualitative properties which are shared by all of the functions $x_t(\omega)$ except an ω set of probability zero. We will prove certain things in full, and mention a few others without proof. A rich source of theorems of this kind is Paul Levy's book [Le]. Throughout the section, a "Brownian motion" means any process satisfying properties (i) to (iv) of Section 20.

    We first consider the large scale behavior of the paths. A good starting point is the law of the iterated logarithm:

Theorem 1. *Let* $\{x_t(\omega)\}$ *be a Brownian motion process,* $0 \le t < \infty$. *Then*

$$P\left(\limsup_{t\to\infty}\frac{x_t}{\sqrt{2t\log\log t}} = 1\right) = 1. \tag{1}$$

Proof. If we replace the continuous variable t by an integral one, (1) becomes a special case of the "law of the iterated logarithm" for sums of independent r.v.'s which was discussed in Section 11. In fact, the random variables in this case—namely, $(x_{i+1} - x_i)$—have a normal distribution with mean 0 and variance 1, and it was really only in this case that the lower bound of Section 11 was proved. (The lower bound was based on Lemma 11.3 which was not proved; in the normal case the conclusion was indicated in Problem 11.3.) It is therefore clear that (1) is true with "$=$" replaced by "$\geq$," for if the lower bound holds as $t \to \infty$ through integers, it is certainly still correct when $t \to \infty$ continuously.

To obtain the upper bound, it is necessary to show that x_t does not fluctuate too widely between successive integral values of t. We will use the following estimate:

Lemma 1. *For any $a > 0$,*

$$P(\max_{0 \leq t \leq 1} x_t > a) \leq 2P(x_1 \geq a - \sqrt{2}). \tag{2}$$

Proof. Let k be any positive integer, and notice that by writing

$$x_{i/2^k} = \sum_{j=0}^{i-1} (x_{(j+1)/2^k} - x_{j/2^k}), \tag{3}$$

we exhibit $x_{i/2^k}$ as the sum of i independent random variables, each normally distributed with mean 0 and variance 2^{-k}. Applying Lemma 2 of Section 11, we obtain

$$P(\max_{i \leq 2^k} x_{i/2^k} > a) \leq 2P(x_1 \geq a - \sqrt{2}). \tag{4}$$

But as k increases, the events on the left side of (4) increase also, and the bound on the right is independent of k. Hence the bound holds for their union, which is the event that $x_t > a$ for some dyadic rational $t \leq 1$. Because x_t is (a.s.) continuous, this event is (almost) the same as the one on the left side of (2), and the bound on its probability follows.

Remark 1. In the same way, we could have derived the "continuous analogue" of Kolmogorov's inequality, namely,

$$P(\max_{0 \leq t \leq 1} |x_t| > a) \leq \frac{1}{a^2}, \qquad a > 0. \tag{5}$$

This is not quite strong enough for the application we want to make next, however.

Remark 2. A reexamination of the proof of Lemma 11.2 shows that when the random variables have distributions symmetric about 0 the right side of (11.10) can be decreased to $2P(S_n \geq a)$. Hence, the "$a - \sqrt{2}$" in (2) above can be replaced by "a." It is worth knowing that $2P(x_1 \geq a)$ turns out to be not only an upper bound but the correct value for the left side of (2); we will prove this indirectly later (Section 26).

With the aid of Lemma 1 we can easily finish the proof of Theorem 1. Using the fact that the right side of (2) is a normal distribution and recalling Lemma 2 of the previous section, we have at once

$$P(\max_{n \leq t \leq n+1} x_t = o(\sqrt{n \log \log n})) = 1; \qquad (6)$$

a very much stronger statement could of course be made. But we know that the upper bound ($\leq$) in (1) holds for all large integral values of t, and combining that with (6) it is clear that (1) is true even when $t \to \infty$ continuously.

Corollary. *The function x_t has* (a.s.) *arbitrarily large zeros.*

Proof. The random variables $\{-x_t(\omega)\}$ are again a Brownian motion to which Theorem 1 applies; hence (1) holds for $-x_t$ as well as for x_t. This means that x_t has both positive and negative values for arbitrarily large t, and continuity does the rest. (Recall the Remark on page 94.)

We turn now to some local properties of the paths. It is natural to ask first if they are differentiable. The quotient

$$\frac{x_{t+h} - x_t}{h}$$

has a normal distribution with mean 0 and variance h^{-1}, and it is not hard to conclude that

$$\lim_{h \to 0} P\left(\left| \frac{x_{t+h} - x_t}{h} \right| \leq M \right) = 0 \qquad (7)$$

for each M. This shows that $P(x_t'$ exists$) = 0$ for each fixed t.

Problem 1. Prove (7), and supply the details for the last assertion above.

This result can be strengthened in several ways. One of these is to find the precise magnitude of the small fluctuations of x_t. The result, due to Khintchine [Kh], is known as the "local law of the iterated logarithm":

Theorem 2. *For each $t_0 > 0$,*

$$P\left(\limsup_{h \to 0+} \frac{x_{t_0+h} - x_{t_0}}{\sqrt{2h \log \log h^{-1}}} = 1\right) = 1. \tag{8}$$

Lemma 2. *Let $\{x_t\}$ be Brownian motion, and define*

$$y_t = \begin{cases} 0 & \text{if } t = 0, \\ t x_{1/t} & \text{if } t > 0. \end{cases} \tag{9}$$

Then $\{y_t\}$ is also a Brownian motion process.

Proof. The continuity of y_t for $t > 0$ is immediate from that of x_t, and continuity at 0 follows from Theorem 1. The simplest way to check properties (ii) and (iii) is to compute the *covariance function* of $\{y_t\}$:

$$
\begin{aligned}
E(y_t y_{t+s}) &= t(t+s) E(x_{t^{-1}} x_{(t+s)^{-1}}) \\
&= t(t+s) \min \left(t^{-1}, (t+s)^{-1}\right) \\
&= t = \min (t, t+s), \quad (10)
\end{aligned}
$$

which is indeed the result expected for Brownian motion (Section 20). It is a fact that for normally-distributed processes (with mean 0) this function characterizes the joint distributions, so that $\{y_t\}$ (like $\{x_t\}$) does satisfy (ii) and (iii). But we have not proved this, so the verification must be carried out "by hand."

We will do the calculation only in the case of two increments for simplicity. We have, for $0 < t_1 < t_2$,

$$
\begin{aligned}
E\{\exp [i\lambda_1 y_{t_1} &+ i\lambda_2 (y_{t_2} - y_{t_1})]\} \\
&= E\{\exp [it_1(\lambda_1 - \lambda_2)(x_{t_1^{-1}} - x_{t_2^{-1}}) \\
&\qquad + i(\lambda_1 t_1 + \lambda_2 (t_2 - t_1)) x_{t_2^{-1}}]\}.
\end{aligned}
$$

But using properties (ii) and (iii) for the x_t process, this becomes

$$\exp\left[-\tfrac{1}{2}t_1{}^2(\lambda_1 - \lambda_2)^2(t_1^{-1} - t_2^{-1}) - \tfrac{1}{2}(\lambda_1 t_1 + \lambda_2(t_2 - t_1))^2 t_2^{-1}\right]$$
$$= \exp\left[-\tfrac{1}{2}\lambda_1{}^2 t_1 - \tfrac{1}{2}\lambda_2{}^2(t_2 - t_1)\right].$$

This last expression is the joint characteristic function of two independent normally distributed r.v.'s, with means 0 and variances t_1 and $t_2 - t_1$ respectively, and in view of the uniqueness theorem discussed in the last section, we see that y_{t_1} and $(y_{t_2} - y_{t_1})$ have the properties required for Brownian motion. Extension of this calculation to k increments completes the proof of the lemma.

The proof of Theorem 2 is immediate from Theorem 1 and Lemma 2. Incidently, the local law of the iterated logarithm was not derived in this manner originally; Lemma 2 is due to P. Levy.

It is easy to deduce the following result:

Corollary. *For each t_0, the function $x_t - x_{t_0}$ has (a.s.) a sequence of zeros converging to t_0 from above.*

In particular, $t_0 = 0$ is not an isolated root of x_t. It would be tempting to conclude that x_t has no isolated zeros, by taking as t_0 a time value for which $x_{t_0} = 0$. This does not follow, however, since t_0 in Theorem 2 must be a fixed value, not a random variable. The conclusion is none the less correct, and its proof is based on the idea that upon reaching 0 at time t_0 the Brownian motion "starts over again" from scratch. The precise statement and proof of this idea rests on the "strong Markov property" which is beyond the scope of this book.

A different strengthening of the fact that, for each t, x_t' (a.s.) does not exist was first obtained by Wiener himself: for almost all paths, there is no value of t at which x_t is differentiable. An even stronger fact is that $x_t + ct$ has (a.s.) no points of increase or decrease for any c; this was proved fairly recently by Dvoretzky, Erdös and Kakutani. We will content ourselves here with a weaker, but easier, result:

Theorem 3. *With probability one, the t set for which x_t' exists has Lebesgue measure 0.*

Since a function of bounded variation is differentiable almost everywhere, we have the interesting

Corollary. *The Brownian path, in one or more dimensions,*[6] *is (a.s.) not rectifiable in any time interval of positive length.*

Proof of Theorem 3. Excluding one technical point, the proof is extremely simple. Define

$$f(\omega, t) = \begin{cases} 1 & \text{if } x_t(\omega) \text{ is differentiable at } t, \\ 0 & \text{otherwise.} \end{cases} \tag{11}$$

Assuming that f is measurable jointly in t and ω (with respect to the product field), we can apply Fubini's theorem and obtain

$$E\left(\int_0^\infty f(\omega, t)\, dt\right) = \int_0^\infty E(f(\omega, t))\, dt = 0, \tag{12}$$

since, for each t, $f(\omega, t) = 0$ a.s. It follows that

$$P\left(\int_0^\infty f(\omega, t)\, dt = 0\right) = 1, \tag{13}$$

which is the same as the conclusion of Theorem 3.

The matter of measurability remains; we will first investigate $x_t(\omega)$ itself. Any function of the form

$$y_t(\omega) = \begin{cases} x_a(\omega) & \text{if } a \leq t < a + h, \quad h, a \geq 0 \text{ constant,} \\ 0, & \text{otherwise,} \end{cases} \tag{14}$$

is certainly measurable. To check this we note that

$$\{(\omega, t): y_t(\omega) > \alpha\} = \begin{cases} \{x_a(\omega) > \alpha \text{ and } a \leq t < a + h\} \\ \qquad\qquad\qquad\qquad\qquad \text{if } \alpha \geq 0, \\ \{x_a(\omega) > \alpha\} \cup \{x_a(\omega) \leq \alpha \text{ and} \\ \qquad\qquad t \notin [a, a + h]\} \text{ if } \alpha < 0. \end{cases}$$

The right side is in one case the product of a measurable ω set with an interval, and in the other case the union of two such products, and hence it is measurable for each α. By adding functions of the form (14), we see that

$$z_t^{(h)}(\omega) = x_{nh}(\omega) \qquad \text{for } nh \leq t < (n + 1)h \tag{15}$$

is measurable. Finally, letting $h \to 0+$ through a countable set of values, and noting that (by continuity)

$$\lim_{h \to 0+} z_t^{(h)}(\omega) = x_t(\omega) \qquad \text{for each } t \geq 0$$

[6] A Brownian motion process in $d > 1$ dimensions is formed by taking independent, one-dimensional Brownian motions as the Cartesian coordinates of a random vector.

except on a set of ω (and hence of (ω, t)) having measure 0, we can conclude the measurability in (ω, t) of $x_t(\omega)$.

The rest is very easy. By standard results on measurability we can say at once that

$$\limsup_{\substack{h \to 0 \\ h \text{ rational}}} \frac{x_{t+h}(\omega) - x_t(\omega)}{h} = D^+ x_t(\omega)$$

is a measurable function; the same is of course true for $D^- x_t(\omega)$. But the set on which two measurable functions agree is necessarily a measurable set. Applying this to D^+ and D^-, we obtain just the set on which $f(\omega, t) = 1$, and this completes the proof.

Remark. The "infinite velocity" posessed by the Brownian particle is, of course, not really paradoxical, for the physical assumptions which led in Section 20 to postulates (ii) and (iii) are certainly not valid when extremely short time intervals are involved. Incidently, there is a more elaborate model of Brownian motion, due to L. S. Ornstein and G. E. Uhlenbeck, in which velocities are finite but accelerations do not exist.

23. *MARKOV TRANSITION FUNCTIONS*

We will now turn to the second approach which was hinted at in Section 20; it affords much greater flexibility in constructing a variety of stochastic processes. The basic idea is to define the desired joint distributions of $\{x_t\}$ for each finite set $(t_1, \ldots, t_k)$ of parameter values, and then to apply Kolmogorov's theorem which was presented in Section 4.

One very important way to obtain the joint distributions is to begin with a *Markov transition function*.[7] This means, by definition, a function $p_t(u, E)$ defined for $t \geq 0$, where u is a point and E a Borel subset of the real line.[8] It is assumed that for each t and u, $p_t(u, \cdot)$ is a probability measure function, that for each t and Borel set E, $p_t(\cdot, E)$ is a Borel measurable func-

---

[7] Some knowledge of discrete *Markov chains* will be helpful for motivation at this point (see, for instance, [F] Chapter XV), but it is not logically required.

[8] It is equally acceptable, and frequently convenient, to assume p_t defined only when $u \in X$, a fixed Borel subset of R^1, and when E is a Borel subset of X. In the other direction, more general spaces—in particular R^k or subsets of R^k—could be used instead of R^1.

tion, and finally that for any u, t, s, E we have

$$p_{t+s}(u, E) = \int_{R^1} p_t(u, dv) p_s(v, E). \tag{1}$$

(The integral is well defined in view of the assumptions above.) The idea behind this definition is to formalize the "Markov principle" which asserts that if the "state" of the process is known at a certain time, then the conditional probability of future events is not changed if additional information about the past is made available. Thus $p_t(u, E)$ is intended to represent the probability that the process goes from u into E after a lapse of time t. Equation (1), which is called the "Chapman-Kolmogorov equation," expresses the idea that this transition in time $t + s$ is composed of a transition to some point v in time t, followed by a transition from v to E in the remaining time s; the latter transition, by the Markov principle, has probability $p_s(v, E)$ which does not depend on u. To make real sense of all this requires a thorough treatment of conditional probabilities, which we will not go into, but we will show (rigorously) how to construct processes from transition functions.

Remark. It should not be thought that only processes of the Markov type are significant; this is entirely false. Another very important general group, for instance, are the *stationary processes*. A stochastic process $\{x_t, -\infty < t < \infty\}$ is said to be (strictly) *stationary* if absolute time plays no role in the sense that

$$P(x_{t_1} \leq u_1, \ldots, x_{t_k} \leq u_k)$$
$$= P(x_{t_1+s} \leq u_1, \ldots, x_{t_k+s} \leq u_k) \tag{2}$$

for all t_i, u_i, and s. Many physical phenomena—generally having to do with a system in some sort of equilibrium—can be represented by stationary processes, and they are very often not Markovian. We will stick to the Markov case in this book, however.

Examples of transition functions. The most important example for our purposes is given by

$$p_t(u, E) = \frac{1}{\sqrt{2\pi t}} \int_E e^{-(v-u)^2/2t} \, dv, \tag{3}$$

for this is the one which leads to the Brownian motion process we have already studied. A closely related case of interest is defined by

$$p_t(u, E) = \frac{1}{\sqrt{2\pi t}} \int_E (e^{-(v-u)^2/2t} + e^{-(v+u)^2/2t})\, dv, \tag{4}$$

where $u \geq 0$ and $E \subset [0, \infty)$. This represents Brownian motion with a *reflecting barrier* at 0; the process can be represented as $\{|x_t|\}$, where $\{x_t\}$ is Wiener's process. Still another simple and yet very useful example is related to the Poisson distribution much as (3) is to the normal:

$$p_t(u, \{u + na\}) = \frac{e^{-ct}(ct)}{n!}, \qquad c > 0, n = 0, 1, 2, \ldots ; a \neq 0 \tag{5}$$

The stochastic process obtained from (5) is called the "Poisson process."

Problem 1. Verify that (3), (4), and (5) define Markov transition functions.

More generally, suppose that $F(u)$ is any infinitely-divisible distribution function (Section 18). By definition, F has a unique "k'th root" with respect to convolution for each k, which we denote by $F_{1/k}$; by convolving these, $F_{p/q}$ can be defined for any rational number. It is a small additional step to prove that for each $t > 0$ there is a distribution F_t satisfying $F_1 = F$ and $F_{t+s} = F_t * F_s$; indeed, we have

$$\int_{-\infty}^{\infty} e^{i\lambda u}\, dF_t(u) = \phi(\lambda)^t, \tag{6}$$

where $\phi(\lambda)$ is the characteristic function of F. Define

$$p_t(u, (-\infty, v]) = F_t(v - u)$$

and determine $p_t(u, E)$ for more general sets from this distribution function in the usual way. This yields a *spatially homogeneous* Markov transition function—one satisfying

$$p_t(u, E) = p_t(u + v, v + E)$$

for all real v. When such a function is used to construct a stochastic process in the way we will soon describe, the resulting process has independent increments.[9] Such processes are sometimes also called "additive" or "differential."

Problem 2. Prove the existence of F_t, and show that the resulting $p_t(x, E)$ is a transition function.

[9] That is, it satisfies postulate (ii) of Section 20.

The construction of a process from a transition function begins in a straightforward way. Any real number u_0 may be chosen as the *initial state;* we will arrange to have $x_0(\omega) = u_0$. (A measure not concentrated at one point could also be specified as an *initial distribution;* the generalization is quite routine.) Let $0 = t_0 < t_1 < \cdots < t_k$, and define a joint distribution function by setting

$$
\begin{aligned}
F_{t_1,\ldots,t_k}(v_1, &\ldots, v_k) \\
&= \int_{-\infty}^{v_1} \cdots \int_{-\infty}^{v_k} p_{t_1}(u_0, du_1) p_{t_2-t_1}(u_1, du_2) \\
&\qquad\qquad \cdots p_{t_k-t_{k-1}}(u_{k-1}, du_k). \quad (7)
\end{aligned}
$$

This function determines a probability measure on R^k which is going to be the joint distribution of the random variables $(x_{t_1}, \ldots, x_{t_k})$. In the same way, a measure is defined for every finite subset of t values.

Theorem 1. *Given any Markov transition function p_t and any real number u_0, there exists a probability space and random variables $\{x_t, t \geq 0\}$ defined on it such that the joint distributions of $(x_{t_1}, \ldots, x_{t_k})$ are determined by*

$$
P(x_{t_1} \leq v_1, \ldots, x_{t_k} \leq v_k) = F_{t_1,\ldots,t_k}(v_1, \ldots, v_k), \quad (8)
$$

where $F_{t_1,\ldots,t_k}$ is defined by (7).

Proof. To apply Theorem 4.1, we have only to verify the hypotheses (4.2) and (4.3). The first of these is trivial. Indeed, we have constructed the desired joint distribution of $x_{t_1}, \ldots, x_{t_k}$ assuming that $t_1 < \cdots < t_k$, and if the random variables are taken in some other order we will use (4.2) as a definition.

The second condition, though easy to prove, is not automatic; assumption (1) must be invoked. We will illustrate the idea with a special, but typical, case: Let $n = 2$ and $m = 1$. An instance of (4.3) is then the assertion that we must have

$$
F_{t_1,t_2,t_3}(v_1, \infty, v_3) = F_{t_1,t_3}(v_1, v_3). \quad (9)
$$

But using the definition (7), this becomes

$$
\begin{aligned}
\int_{-\infty}^{v_1} \int_{-\infty}^{\infty} \int_{-\infty}^{v_3} &p_{t_1}(u_0, du_1) p_{t_2-t_1}(u_1, du_2) p_{t_3-t_2}(u_2, du_3) \\
&= \int_{-\infty}^{v_1} \int_{-\infty}^{v_3} p_{t_1}(u_0, du_1) p_{t_3-t_1}(u_1, du_3), \quad (10)
\end{aligned}
$$

which is easily seen to be true by applying (1) to the integration with respect to the variable u_2. We can now assert that Theorem 4.1 applies, and it yields the conclusion we seek.

Let us consider the special case when $u_0 = 0$ and the transition function is the one given in (3). The following result is neither surprising nor very hard to establish:

Problem 3. Prove that in this case the random variables $\{x_t\}$ guaranteed by Theorem 1 satisfy the axioms (i), (ii), and (iii) of Section 20.

Do we now necessarily have Brownian motion? Unfortunately, the set

$$C_0 = \{\omega \in \Omega : x_t(\omega) \text{ is continuous in } t \text{ for all } t \geq 0\} \quad (11)$$

is not measurable! That is, C_0 does not belong to the Borel field $\mathcal{B}$ of Theorem 4.1, which was, it will be recalled, the smallest σ field containing all the Borel cylinder sets.

To understand this difficulty we will look at an example due to J. L. Doob. Let

$$u_0 = 0; \qquad p_t(x, E) = \begin{cases} 1 & \text{if } 0 \in E, \\ 0, & \text{otherwise.} \end{cases} \quad (12)$$

This is the transition function of a "process" which starts at 0 and stays there; the random variables x_t in this case must satisfy

$$P(x_t = 0) = 1 \text{ for each } t \geq 0. \quad (13)$$

We now consider a peculiar way of constructing these random variables. Let $\Omega = [0, 1]$ with P being Lebesgue measure, and define

$$x_t(\omega) = \begin{cases} 1 & \text{if } t = \omega, \\ 0, & \text{otherwise.} \end{cases} \quad (14)$$

It is clear that (13) is satisfied, and yet the probability that x_t is continuous, $0 \leq t \leq 1$, is zero. There is an obvious alternative construction which makes this probability have the value one. (Ω can consist of a single point!) Each method of constructing $\{x_t(\omega)\}$ can be used to introduce a measure into the function space defined in (4.4); the second will yield a measure concentrated entirely on the function $x_t \equiv 0$, while the first will be nonatomic. The two will agree on all cylinder sets because of (13), and so they will agree on $\mathcal{B}$. But the measures, as we have seen, do not agree on C_0, and this proves that $C_0 \not\in \mathfrak{B}$.

Problem 4. Show that the function

$$f(\omega) = \sup_{0 \leq t \leq 1} x_t(\omega) \tag{15}$$

is not measurable with respect to the field $\mathfrak{B}$ generated by the cylinder sets.

24. CONTINUITY OF PATHS

The measurability problems we have been discussing arise because the parameter set $[0, \infty)$ is not denumerable. One way out of our difficulties lies in restricting attention at first to a dense denumerable subset, and then showing that the definition of the functions x_t can be extended to the whole of $0 \leq t < \infty$. in a natural way. This approach, in effect, has been carried out in great generality by J. L. Doob in his theory of "separability" of stochastic processes [Do]. We will use it in a much more special context to construct a class of Markov processes with continuous paths including (again) Brownian motion.

The goal of this section will be to prove the following result, due to J. R. Kinney and E. B. Dynkin independently:

Theorem 1. *Let p_t be a Markov transition function on R^1 and suppose that, for each $\epsilon > 0$,*

$$p_t(x, R^1 - [x - \epsilon, x + \epsilon]) \leq k_\epsilon(t), \tag{1}$$

where the bounding function $k_\epsilon(t)$ is independent of x, decreases as $t \to 0$ and satisfies $\lim_{t \to 0} t^{-1} k_\epsilon(t) = 0$.[10] Then there is a probability space and a family of random variables $\{\mathbf{x}_t(\omega), t \geq 0\}$ such that condition (8) of the last section is satisfied and, in addition, such that $\mathbf{x}_t(\omega)$ is everywhere continuous in t for almost all ω.

Proof. First we apply the result of the last section to construct a probability space $(\Omega, \mathfrak{B}, P)$ on which random variables $\{x_t(\omega), t \geq 0\}$ are defined which satisfy (23.8). Let S denote

---

[10] It is the same thing to say simply that $p_t(x, R^1 - [x - \epsilon, x + \epsilon]) = o(t)$ uniformly in x.

the nonnegative dyadic rationals $\{i/2^n\}$. We are going, for a while, to restrict our attention to parameter values in S; since S is denumerable we will then not meet measurability difficulties like those encountered above. In fact we have the following:

Lemma 1. *For almost all* $\omega \in \Omega$, $x_t(\omega)$ *with* $t \in S$ *is the restriction to* S *of an everywhere continuous function.*

Proof. For any $\epsilon > 0$, we will show that

$$\lim_{\delta \to 0} P\left(\sup_{\substack{|t-s| < \delta \\ t,s \in S \cap [0,\,1]}} |x_t(\omega) - x_s(\omega)| > \epsilon \right) = 0. \tag{2}$$

Thus given a particular $\epsilon > 0$ there is only an ω set of measure 0 on which there does not exist a suitable $\delta > 0$. Letting $\epsilon \searrow 0$ through a denumerable set, and excluding each of the resulting exceptional sets of probability zero, it is clear that (2) implies $x_t(\omega)$ to be almost surely uniformly continuous over $S \cap [0, 1]$, and hence to be the restriction to S of a continuous function on $[0, 1]$. The extension from $[0, 1]$ to $[0, \infty)$ offers no difficulty.

It is easy to see that (2) holds if, for every $\epsilon > 0$,

$$\lim_{n \to \infty} P(\max_{i < 2^n} \sup_{t \in S \cap \left[\frac{i}{2^n},\, \frac{i+1}{2^n}\right]} |x_t - x_{i/2^n}| > \epsilon) = 0, \tag{3}$$

and (3) will be our actual point of departure.[11] We note that the event in question in (3) is actually a union of the events that the sup exceeds ϵ in the i'th interval. If, then, we establish that for each $i < 2^n$

$$P\left(\sup_{t \in S \cap \left[\frac{i}{2^n},\, \frac{i+1}{2^n}\right]} |x_t - x_{i/2^n}| > \epsilon \right) \leq 2k_{\epsilon/2}(2^{-n}), \tag{4}$$

we can conclude that the probability in (3) is at most $2^{n+1}k_{\epsilon/2}(2^{-n})$. Equation (3), and the lemma, will then follow because of the growth assumption on $k_\epsilon(t)$. We proceed to derive (4).

Fix $i < 2^n$, and let A denote the event whose probability is written on the left side of (4). Let m be a positive integer, and

---

[11] To obtain (2) with a particular ϵ_0 from (3), the "ϵ" in (3) should be chosen less than $\epsilon_0/3$.

define

$$A_m = \left\{ \omega \colon \left| x_t - x_{i/2^n} \right| > \epsilon \text{ for some} \right.$$

$$\left. t = \frac{i}{2^n} + \frac{j}{2^{n+m}}, \qquad 0 \le j \le 2^m \right\}. \quad (5)$$

Now, as m increases the sets A_m also increase, and their union is A. It is thus enough to establish (4) for each A_m, because the bound is independent of m and so will hold in the limit. But we have

$$P(A_m) \le P\left(\sup \left| x_t - x_{i/2^n} \right| > \epsilon \text{ and } \left| x_{(i+1)/2^n} - x_{i/2^n} \right| \le \frac{\epsilon}{2} \right)$$

$$+ P\left(\left| x_{(i+1)/2^n} - x_{i/2^n} \right| > \frac{\epsilon}{2} \right), \quad (6)$$

where "sup" means the maximum over the t values allowed in (5). Part of this can be easily estimated. In fact,

$$P(\left| x_{t+s} - x_s \right| > \eta) = \int_{R^1} p_s(u_0, du) p_t(u, R^1 - [u - \eta, u + \eta])$$
$$\le k_\eta(t) \quad (7)$$

using (1), so that the second term on the right in (6) is less than $k_{\epsilon/2}(2^{-n})$.

The first term in (6) can be rewritten to advantage by singling out the first allowed value of t at which ϵ is exceeded:

$$P\left(\sup \left| x_t - x_{t_0} \right| > \epsilon \text{ and } \left| x_{t_0 + 2^{-n}} - x_{t_0} \right| \le \frac{\epsilon}{2} \right)$$

$$= \sum_{j=1}^{2^m} P\left(\left| x_{t_0 + l\tau} - x_{t_0} \right| > \epsilon \text{ for the first time when } l = j \right.$$

$$\left. \text{and } \left| x_{t_0 + 2^{-n}} - x_{t_0} \right| \le \frac{\epsilon}{2} \right), \quad (8)$$

where $\tau = 2^{-(n+m)}$ and $t_0 = i/2^n$.

Each term of the sum can be expressed by a multiple integral containing a factor which represents the transition from some state distant at least ϵ from x_{t_0} to a final position within $\epsilon/2$. This transition takes place in a time interval less than 2^{-n}, and so the factor is bounded by $k_{\epsilon/2}(2^{-n})$. After this factor is removed, the probabilities sum to at most 1. For instance, we can write this out for $j = 2$ as follows:

$$P\left(\left|x_{t_0+\tau} - x_{t_0}\right| \le \epsilon, \left|x_{t_0+2\tau} - x_{t_0}\right| > \epsilon, \left|x_{t_0+2^{-n}} - x_{t_0}\right| \le \frac{\epsilon}{2}\right)$$

$$= \iiint_Q p_{t_0}(u_0, du_1) p_\tau(u_1, du_2) p_\tau(u_2, du_3)$$

$$\cdot p_{2^{-n}-2\tau}\left(u_3, \left[u_1 - \frac{\epsilon}{2}, u_1 + \frac{\epsilon}{2}\right]\right), \quad (9)$$

where the region of integration Q is described by

$$u_1 \in (-\infty, \infty); \qquad u_2 \in [u_1 - \epsilon, u_1 + \epsilon];$$
$$u_3 \notin [u_1 - \epsilon, u_1 + \epsilon]. \quad (10)$$

The last factor in the integrand of (9) is at most $k_{\epsilon/2}(2^{-n} - 2\tau) \le k_{\epsilon/2}(2^{-n})$ (monotonicity was assumed), and so the left side of (9) is at most

$$k_{\epsilon/2}(2^{-n}) P(\left|x_{t_0+\tau} - x_{t_0}\right| \le \epsilon, \left|x_{t_0+2\tau} - x_{t_0}\right| > \epsilon).$$

Summing this on j (remember that $j = 2$ in our illustration) we obtain for the left side of (8) the bound

$$k_{\epsilon/2}(2^{-n}) P(\sup \left|x_t - x_{t_0}\right| > \epsilon) \le k_{\epsilon/2}(2^{-n}).$$

Returning to (6), and using the bounds now available for each part, we have

$$P(A_m) \le 2k_{\epsilon/2}(2^{-n}) \qquad \text{for each } m, \quad (11)$$

which yields (4) and hence proves the lemma.

To finish the proof of Theorem 1 is quite easy. We will *define* new random variables $\mathbf{x}_t$ on our space $(\Omega, \mathcal{B}, P)$ as follows:

$$\mathbf{x}_t(\omega) = \begin{cases} x_t(\omega) & \text{for } t \in S, \\ \limsup_{\substack{s \to t+ \\ s \in S}} x_s(\omega), & t \notin S. \end{cases} \quad (12)$$

Because of Lemma 1, the "lim sup" is really a limit a.s. and $\mathbf{x}_t(\omega)$ is, for almost all ω, an everywhere continuous function of t. The r.v.'s $\{\mathbf{x}_t(\omega)\}$, we claim, will satisfy the assertions of the theorem.

The only thing that still needs to be checked is that the $\mathbf{x}_t$ have the right joint distributions, given by (23.8). For $t \in S$ this is guaranteed by Theorem 23.1, but what if $t \notin S$? We will settle this point by showing that for each $t \geq 0$,

$$P(\mathbf{x}_t(\omega) = x_t(\omega)) = 1. \tag{13}$$

In verifying (13) clearly only values of $t \notin S$ need be considered. We use an earlier (easy) estimate (7) to write

$$P(|x_t - x_s| > \epsilon) \leq k_\epsilon(s - t), \tag{14}$$

where $t < s$, $s \in S$ and $\epsilon > 0$ is arbitrary. Since $k_\epsilon(u) = o(1)$ as $u \to 0$ (we actually assumed $o(u)$), (14) shows that x_t is a limit in probability of x_s as $s \to t+$. But since $\mathbf{x}_t$ is also such a limit (by definition (12) and the lemma), $\mathbf{x}_t$ must equal x_t a.s. and (13) is proved. It is then clear, since x_t satisfies (23.8), that $\mathbf{x}_t$ does so too; this completes the proof of Theorem 1.

Problem 1. Complete the second proof of the existence of the Brownian motion process by verifying that the transition function (23.3) satisfies the hypotheses of Theorem 1.

Problem 2. In the Brownian case (23.3) the proof of Theorem 1 can be considerably simplified. Derive the estimate

$$P(\sup_{t \in (r,\, s) \cap S} (x_t - x_r) > a) \leq 2P(x_s - x_r > a)$$

(recall Lemma 1 of Section 22 and Remark 2 following it) and use it to give a shorter proof of Lemma 1 above.

Problem 3. Show that

$$p_t(0, \{0\}) = e^{-t}; \qquad p_t(0, \{1\}) = 1 - e^{-t}; \qquad p_t(1, \{1\}) = 1$$

defines a Markov transition function on the subset $\{0, 1\}$ of R^1, that condition (1) holds with $k_\epsilon(t) = O(t)$ instead of $o(t)$, and that if $u_0 = 0$ no process with a.s. continuous paths corresponds to (1).

Remark. Among the "spatially homogeneous" transition functions discussed in the previous section, none which are essentially different from the Brownian case [12] satisfy the hypotheses of Theorem 1; the others do not, in fact, lead to processes with continuous paths. It is desirable to have an effective means of constructing such processes too, and we will state without proof a result by Kinney along these lines:

[12] To be precise, those for which the distributions $p_t(x, \cdot)$ are neither of the normal type nor degenerate.

Theorem 2. *Suppose the conditions of Theorem 1 are satisfied except that $k_\epsilon(t)$ is required only to be $o(1)$ instead of $o(t)$ for each $\epsilon > 0$. Then there is a probability space bearing random variables $\{\mathbf{x}_t(\omega), t \geq 0\}$ such that (23.8) is satisfied and that $\mathbf{x}_t(\omega)$, for almost all ω, is right continuous everywhere and has a left-hand limit at each $t > 0$.*

Problem 4. Show that spatially homogeneous transition functions satisfy the assumptions of Theorem 2. What do the path functions $\mathbf{x}_t$ look like when $p_t(x, E)$ is given by (23.5)?

25. KOLMOGOROV'S EQUATIONS

We have seen how a transition function which satisfies a certain condition ((24.1) with $k_\epsilon(t) = o(t)$) leads to a "Markovian" stochastic process with a.s. continuous paths. As yet, however, we have basically only one example of such a transition function. We will now discuss ways in which many other such functions can be constructed by solving certain parabolic partial differential equations.

Let us begin with the Brownian motion case. Here $p_t(x, E)$, defined in (23.3), has the density

$$f(t, x, y) = \frac{1}{\sqrt{2\pi t}}\, e^{-(y-x)^2/2t}, \qquad t > 0. \qquad (1)$$

This function is, for each x, the *fundamental solution* of the classical "heat" or "diffusion" equation

$$\frac{\partial f}{\partial t} = \frac{1}{2}\frac{\partial^2 f}{\partial y^2}. \qquad (2)$$

This means that the right side of (1) is a solution of (2) for $t > 0$, and that as $t \to 0$, the measures defined by using $f(t, x, \cdot)$ as a density converge weakly to a unit mass at x. This method of looking at the problem makes (2) the so-called *forward equation* of the Wiener process: For fixed initial state, the density of the distribution of x_t satisfies a parabolic differential equation.

There is another approach, which at first appears less natural but turns out to be both easier to work with and more general. This is, basically, to consider the terminal state to be fixed, and vary the initial state and the elapsed time. In the case of

(1) the change in point of view seems deceptively trivial; if y rather than x is fixed, f is clearly still a fundamental solution of (2) (with $\partial^2/\partial x^2$ in place of $\partial^2/\partial y^2$). A slightly different way to put this is as follows: let $\xi(x)$ be any bounded, continuous function on R^1 and define

$$\phi(t, x) = \int_{R^1} \xi(y) f(t, x, y) \, dy. \tag{3}$$

Then ϕ satisfies the heat equation (2) (with x replacing y) and also the intial condition $\phi(0, x) = \xi(x)$. In this context (2) is the *backward equation* of the process.

More generally, let $p_t(x, E)$ be any transition function. The "forward" approach seeks to find a functional equation—a differential equation if possible—satisfied by the density of the measure $p_t(x, \cdot)$ for fixed x; the choice of x will enter only through the *initial condition* that as $t \to 0+$, the solution should converge to a unit mass at x. This method was known to physicists such as Smoluchowski even before the work of Wiener, and led to useful results about, for instance, Brownian motion subject to outside forces or inhomogenieties in the medium.

The "backward" approach was introduced by Kolmogorov in 1931 in a famous paper which first systematically surveyed the whole question. Define, as in (3),

$$\phi(t, x) = \int_{R^1} \xi(y) p_t(x, dy) \tag{4}$$

where ξ is bounded and continuous. We will try to find an equation satisfied by these functions ϕ; this time ξ will enter through the condition $\phi(0+, x) = \xi(x)$. If the equation, subject to this condition, can be solved for every ξ it will be possible to reconstruct the transition function, although, of course, it is not given in quite as intuitive a form as in the forward case. The advantages of the backward method lie in its greater generality and theoretical simplicity, and it has come to occupy the dominant position in the mathematical literature.

We will now derive a (backward) "diffusion equation" satisfied by the functions ϕ defined in (4). Since we are interested in continuous paths, and so in a transition probability satisfying the conditions of Theorem 24.1 or something close, it is natural to assume at least that

$$\lim_{t \to 0+} \frac{1}{t} \, p_t(x, R^1 - [x - \epsilon, x + \epsilon]) = 0 \text{ for each } \epsilon > 0, \text{ each } x. \tag{5}$$

It then does not seem unreasonable to also require that the limits

$$\lim_{t \to 0+} \frac{1}{t} \int_{x-\epsilon}^{x+\epsilon} p_t(x, dy)(y - x) = a(x) \qquad (6)$$

and

$$\lim_{t \to 0+} \frac{1}{t} \int_{x-\epsilon}^{x+\epsilon} p_t(x, dy)(y - x)^2 = b(x) \geq 0 \qquad (7)$$

exist for each x, for some (and hence, because of (5), for all) $\epsilon > 0$. Physically, $a(x)$ may be thought of as an average (over ω) instantaneous (with respect to t) velocity when the process is "at x"; $b(x)$ has a similar interpretation as a variance. Finally, we have to assume that the function ϕ has a continuous (in t and x) second partial derivative with respect to x, for all $t > 0$.

Problem 1. Verify these assumptions in the case of the Brownian motion transition function (23.3), with $a(x) = 0$ and $b(x) = 1$.

Theorem 1. *If the above conditions hold, then the function ϕ defined in (4) satisfies the differential equation*

$$\frac{\partial \phi}{\partial t} = a(x) \frac{\partial \phi}{\partial x} + \frac{b(x)}{2} \frac{\partial^2 \phi}{\partial x^2}, \qquad t > 0, \qquad (8)$$

and the initial condition

$$\lim_{t \to 0+} \phi(t, x) = \xi(x), \qquad x \in R^1. \qquad (9)$$

Proof. We will write down the difference quotient which leads to $\partial \phi / \partial t$, and show that its limit exists. Assume first that $h > 0$. Our method will use the Chapman-Kolmogorov equation (23.1) to write p_{t+h} in terms of p_t and p_h; clearly, there are two ways of doing this. The one appropriate to the "backward" approach is as follows:

$$\phi(t + h, x) = \int\int p_h(x, dy) p_t(y, dz) \xi(z) = \int p_h(x, dy) \phi(t, y),$$

which leads to

$$\frac{\phi(t + h, x) - \phi(t, x)}{h} = \frac{1}{h} \int_{-\infty}^{\infty} p_h(x, dy) \{\phi(t, y) - \phi(t, x)\}.$$

$$(10)$$

To take the limit as $h \to 0$, we first observe that by (5), using the fact that ϕ is bounded (by sup $|\xi(y)|$), we can rewrite (10) as

$$\frac{\phi(t+h, x) - \phi(t, x)}{h} = \frac{1}{h} \int_{x-\epsilon}^{x+\epsilon} p_h(x, dy) \{\phi(t, y) - \phi(t, x)\}$$
$$+ o(1) \quad (11)$$

for each $\epsilon > 0$. Next, using the assumptions about the smoothness of ϕ, we have

$$\phi(t, y) = \phi(t, x) + (y - x)\phi_x(t, x) + \frac{(y - x)^2}{2} \phi_{xx}(t, x)$$
$$+ r(t, y)(y - x)^2 \quad (12)$$

by Taylor's theorem, where $r(t, y) \to 0$ as $y \to x$. We are going to substitute (12) into the right side of (11), and then use (6) and (7). The error term in (12) leads to an integral bounded by the quantity

$$\max_{y \in [x-\epsilon, x+\epsilon]} |r(t, y)| \frac{1}{h} \int_{x-\epsilon}^{x+\epsilon} p_h(x, dy)(y - x)^2,$$

whose lim sup as $h \to 0+$ is at most max $|r(t, y)|b(x)$. This is, of course, arbitrarily small if ϵ is suitably chosen. Putting all this together we obtain

$$\lim_{h \to 0+} \frac{\phi(t+h, x) - \phi(t, x)}{h} = a(x)\phi_x(t, x)$$
$$+ \frac{b(x)}{2} \phi_{xx}(t, x). \quad (13)$$

We must still consider the case $h < 0$. This is handled in essentially the same way, beginning with the relation

$$\frac{\phi(t+h, x) - \phi(t, x)}{h} = \frac{1}{h} \int_{-\infty}^{\infty} p_{|h|}(x, dy) \{\phi(t+h, x)$$
$$- \phi(t+h, y)\}. \quad (14)$$

The analysis is much as before, using (12), except that in obtaining the limit as $h \to 0$ it is now necessary to invoke the joint continuity of ϕ_x and ϕ_{xx} in t and x; in particular, we need the fact that $r(t, y) \to 0$ as $y \to x$ uniformly in t over finite

intervals.   The details of this argument, as well as the proof
of condition (9), will be left as exercises.

Problem 2.   Complete the calculation of

$$\lim_{h \to 0-} \frac{\phi(t + h, x) - \phi(t, x)}{h}$$

along the lines sketched in the last paragraph.

Problem 3.   Assuming only that $p_t(x, R^1 - [x - \epsilon, x + \epsilon]) \to 0$ as
$t \to 0+$ for each $\epsilon > 0$, verify that (9) holds for every bounded, continuous function ξ.

We will not derive the forward equation analogous to (8),
but the reader may still want to know what it looks like.
Assumptions (5), (6), and (7) are again required, together with
"regularity" conditions more stringent than those needed in
the backward case; to begin with, $p_t(x, E)$ must have a density
$f(t, x, y)$ which is twice continuously differentiable in y.   The
equation satisfied by f, for fixed x, turns out to be

$$\frac{\partial f}{\partial t} = \frac{1}{2} \frac{\partial^2}{\partial y^2} (b(y)f) - \frac{\partial}{\partial y} (a(y)f); \qquad (15)$$

the operator on the right is the formal adjoint of the one in (8).
It is apparent that (15) is less general than the backward
equations, for it is quite possible that the functions a and b may
not be differentiable.

We have shown that a transition function satisfying certain
conditions generates solutions of the system (8) and (9).   However, the most obvious applications are in the opposite direction; given the functions $a(x)$ and $b(x)$, we would like to construct $p_t(x, E)$ by solving (8).   This was done before 1920 in
special cases (using the forward equation (15) instead of (8)),
but the first general treatment was given by W. Feller in 1936.
By a method of successive approximation, Feller showed, under
some rather restrictive conditions on $a(x)$ and $b(x)$, that there
is a unique bounded solution ϕ to (8) and (9) for each ξ, and
that these functions ϕ come via (4) from a transition probability
function.[13]   It was first proved by R. Fortet in 1943 that these

[13] This is not quite as Feller put it, but equivalent.   The hypotheses of Theorem 1, incidently, are essentially those of Feller's 1936
paper rather than Kolmogorov's.

probabilities correspond to processes with continuous paths. This is, in essence, where the theory of diffusion stood at the end of the "classical period." Since 1950, it has been completely transformed by the work of Ito, Feller, Doob, Dynkin, and many others. We will not attempt to give here any systematic treatment of the modern period in diffusion—and Markov process—theory, but refer (or defer) to the recent books by Dynkin and by Ito and McKean, which give a comprehensive and up to date account of the general theory.

26. BROWNIAN MOTION AND LIMIT THEOREMS

In these last sections we return to the particular case of Brownian motion in order to sketch a few more recent developments. Proofs will be often either incomplete or omitted entirely as we try to briefly survey some of the most interesting new aspects of the theory.

In 1946, P. Erdös and M. Kac gave a new method for proving several limit theorems concerning independent random variables. The first of their results was as follows: *Let X_i, $i = 1, 2, \ldots$, be independent, identically distributed random variables having mean 0 and variance 1, and let $S_n = X_1 + \cdots + X_n$. Then*

$$\lim_{n \to \infty} P(\max (0, S_1, S_2, \ldots, S_n) \leq \alpha \sqrt{n}) = \sigma_1(\alpha), \quad (1)$$

where σ_1 is the "truncated normal" distribution function

$$\sigma_1(\alpha) = \begin{cases} \sqrt{\dfrac{2}{\pi}} \displaystyle\int_0^\alpha \exp(-t^2/2) & \text{for } \alpha \geq 0, \\ 0 & \text{for } \alpha < 0. \end{cases} \quad (2)$$

The proof used what the authors called an "invariance principle." The idea was to show first that *if* (1) holds for *some* sequence of random variables $\{X_i\}$ satisfying the assumptions, then it must hold in general; the existence and value of the limit are independent of the choice of the distribution of X_i. When this invariance principle is established, it is only necessary to find some convenient special case in which the limit can be determined to complete the proof of the general theorem.

There is one example for which the derivation of (1) and (2) is easy. Let X_i be the "coin-tossing" r.v.'s equal to $+1$ or -1

with probability 1/2. In this case, the so-called "reflection principle" states that

$$P(\max (S_1, \ldots, S_n) \geq k) = 2P(S_n > k) + P(S_n = k)$$
$$\text{for each } k > 0. \quad (3)$$

The proof of (3) lies in recognizing that each sequence $(X_1, \ldots, X_n)$ for which $S_n > k$ has a unique counterpart (with equal probability 2^{-n}) obtained by "reflection" around the line $y = k$ after the first time that $S_j = k$, so that the "reflected" maximum is still $\geq k$ but now $S_n < k$. (See Fig. 1.) From

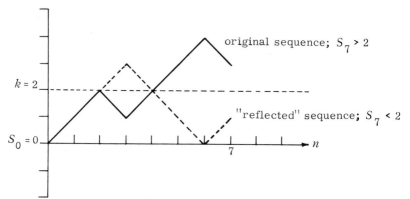

original sequence; $S_7 > 2$

$k = 2$

"reflected" sequence; $S_7 < 2$

$S_0 = 0$

Figure 1

(3), it is easy to obtain (1) and (2) for this example, and by the invariance principle we can conclude that they hold in general.

Problem 1. Give the proof of (3) in full, and then use the De Moivre-Laplace limit theorem (Section 14 or 15) and (3) to establish (1) and (2) for the coin-tossing case.

The idea of Erdös and Kac was extended and completed by M. Donsker a few years later. The simplest way to state the result [14] is to define a continuous random function on [0, 1] in terms of $(X_1, \ldots, X_n)$ by setting

$$x_t^{(n)}(\omega) = \frac{S_i(\omega)}{\sqrt{n}} \qquad \text{when } t = \frac{i}{n}, i \leq n, \quad (4)$$

[14] This formulation is due to Yu. V. Prokhorov, who has contributed much to the subject.

and determining $x_t^{(n)}$ for the other values of t in [0, 1] by linear interpolation between these points. Let C denote the space of continuous functions on [0, 1], together with the metric

$$\rho(x, y) = \max_{0 \leq t \leq 1} |x(t) - y(t)|.$$

It is not hard to show that the random functions $x_t^{(n)}$ induce probability measures P_n on the Borel field [15] of C through the obvious mapping

$$P_n(E) = P(\{\omega: x_t^{(n)}(\omega) \in E\}),$$

where $(\Omega, \mathfrak{B}, P)$ is the probability space of $X_1, X_2, \ldots$. Similarly the Wiener process induces a measure W on the Borel sets of C. The main result can now be simply stated:

Theorem (Donsker). *Provided $X_1, X_2, \ldots$ are independent and identically distributed with mean 0 and variance 1, the measures P_n converge weakly to W.*

The weak convergence asserted in this theorem (defined in Section 12) can be rephrased in ways which are often more useful. One of these is as follows:

Corollary. *Let f be a real valued function on C which is Borel measurable and continuous at every point of C except a set of Wiener measure 0. Then the distributions of the random variables $f(x_t^{(n)}(\omega))$ converge weakly to the distribution of $f(x_t(\omega))$, where $x_t(\omega)$ is the Brownian motion process.*

For example, the function

$$m(x_t) = \max_{0 \leq t \leq 1} x_t \tag{5}$$

is continuous in the uniform topology at every function $x_t \in C$. But

$$m(x_t^{(n)}) = \frac{\max (0, S_1, \ldots, S_n)}{\sqrt{n}}, \tag{6}$$

---

[15] The metric determines the class of open sets; the members of the smallest σ field containing all open sets are the "Borel sets" in this case.

so that the corollary asserts the existence of the limiting distribution in (1) and the fact that $\sigma_1(\alpha)$ is the distribution of the random variable $\max_{0 \leq t \leq 1} x_t(\omega)$, where $\{x_t(\omega)\}$ is Brownian motion. Since we have already obtained the expression (2) as the limit in a special case, we obtain a (rather indirect) verification of the assertion made in Section 22 about the distribution of the maximum displacement of the Brownian process.

There are, obviously, a vast number of limit theorems for the sequence of sums $\{S_n\}$ implicitly contained in Theorem 1 and its corollary. It is perhaps worth stressing that these are of a quite different nature from the theorems of Chapter 3. For instance, we have explicitly the distribution of S_n once given the distribution of the variables X_i, or at least we have its characteristic function. There is, however, no simple formula for the characteristic function of $M_n = \max\ (0, S_1, \ldots, S_n)$, and considerable recent work by F. Spitzer and several others has revealed the difficulty of this and related problems. In view of this situation, the knowledge of the limiting distribution for many functionals of $(S_1, \ldots, S_n)$ is especially striking.

One more example—the famous "arc-sine" law. *Let X_1, X_2, . . . be as before, and denote by N_n the number of positive terms among $(S_1, \ldots, S_n)$. Then*

$$\lim_{n \to \infty} P(N_n \leq nx) = \frac{2}{\pi} \sin^{-1} \sqrt{x}, \qquad 0 \leq x \leq 1. \qquad (7)$$

The proof follows the lines sketched above. For any continuous function x_t, define

$$N(x_t) = m\{t \in (0, 1) : x_t > 0\}, \quad m \text{ Lebesgue measure.} \qquad (8)$$

This function satisfies the requirement of the corollary above; it can fail to be continuous only at those functions in C whose zeros form a set of positive Lebesgue measure, and these functions have Wiener measure 0. (That is easily proved by the argument used for Theorem 22.3.) If we apply N to the random function $x_t{}^{(n)}$ defined in (4), the result is "almost" N_n/n; the difference can be proved to tend to zero in probability. (There are other ways to get around this minor difficulty too.) Finally, the distribution of $N(x_t)$ can be evaluated with $x_t(\omega)$ Wiener's process, as was done by P. Levy. Alternatively, the limiting distribution can again be obtained in the special case of coin tossing (see [F]). If either of these special results is available, the other calculation—and the general result (7)—then follows from Donsker's theorem.

A complete discussion and proof of Donsker's theorem is rather too lengthy for inclusion here. Instead, we will give the proof for the first of the above special cases. The general result can, after some preliminary lemmas on weak convergence of measures on C, be obtained by arguments quite similar to those below, although a bit more complicated.

Theorem 1. *If* X_1, X_2, . . . *are independent, identically distributed random variables with mean* 0 *and variance* 1, *then the distribution of* $M_n/\sqrt{n}$ *converges weakly as* $n \to \infty$ *to the distribution of* $\max_{0 \le t \le 1} x_t$, *where* $\{x_t\}$ *is Brownian motion.*

Proof. Let k be a "large" fixed integer, and define $n_i = [in/k]$, $i = 0, 1, \ldots, k$. In addition to M_n we will consider

$$M_n^{(k)} = \max (0, S_{n_1}, \ldots, S_{n_k}). \tag{9}$$

The idea of the proof is that the limiting distribution of $M_n^{(k)}$ can be related to Brownian motion rather simply, since only a fixed finite number of variables are involved. Then it will be shown that for large k, M_n and $M_n^{(k)}$ are "almost the same." We take up these points in order.

From our assumptions, and using Theorem 15.1 (central limit theorem), it follows easily that

$$\lim_{n \to \infty} P \left(\frac{S_{n_1}}{\sqrt{n}} \le u_1, \frac{S_{n_2} - S_{n_1}}{\sqrt{n}} \le u_2, \ldots, \frac{S_{n_k} - S_{n_{k-1}}}{\sqrt{n}} \le u_k \right)$$

$$= \prod_{i=1}^{k} \Phi_{k^{-1}}(u_i), \tag{10}$$

where $\Phi_{k^{-1}}$ is the normal distribution function with mean 0, variance k^{-1}. The right side of (10), however, is equal to

$$P(x_{1/k} \le u_1, x_{2/k} - x_{1/k} \le u_2, \ldots, x_1 - x_{(k-1)/k} \le u_k), \tag{11}$$

where $\{x_t(\omega)\}$ is Brownian motion; this is immediate from the definition in Section 20. It follows [16] that the joint distribu-

---

[16] This depends on a lemma about weak convergence in R^k, whose

tion of $(S_{n_1}/\sqrt{n}, \ldots, S_{n_k}/\sqrt{n})$ converges weakly on R^k to the joint distribution of $(x_{1/k}, x_{2/k}, \ldots, x_1)$. In particular we have

$$\lim_{n \to \infty} P\left(\frac{M_n^{(k)}}{\sqrt{n}} \leq \alpha\right) = P(\max_{0 \leq i \leq k} x_{i/k}(\omega) \leq \alpha), \qquad (12)$$

where on the right side $x_t(\omega)$ is again the Wiener process.[17]

Now we will compare $M_n^{(k)}$ and M_n. To begin with, it is obvious that $M_n^{(k)} \leq M_n$, and so

$$P\left(\frac{M_n}{\sqrt{n}} \leq \alpha\right) \leq P\left(\frac{M_n^{(k)}}{\sqrt{n}} \leq \alpha\right) \qquad (13)$$

for all α. To get a lower bound, we first choose an $\epsilon > 0$ and write

$$\begin{aligned}
P(M_n > \alpha \sqrt{n}) &= P(M_n > \alpha \sqrt{n} \text{ and } M_n^{(k)} > (\alpha - \epsilon) \sqrt{n}) \\
&\quad + P(M_n > \alpha \sqrt{n} \text{ and } M_n^{(k)} \leq (\alpha - \epsilon) \sqrt{n}) \\
&\leq P(M_n^{(k)} > (\alpha - \epsilon) \sqrt{n}) \\
&\quad + P(M_n > \alpha \sqrt{n} \text{ and } M_n^{(k)} \leq (\alpha - \epsilon) \sqrt{n}). \quad (14)
\end{aligned}$$

We will get our estimate by proving the last term to be small. The details follow a somewhat familiar pattern:

$$\begin{aligned}
P(M_n &> \alpha \sqrt{n} \text{ and } M_n^{(k)} \leq (\alpha - \epsilon) \sqrt{n}) \\
&= \sum_{i=1}^{n} P(S_1 \leq \alpha \sqrt{n}, \ldots, S_{i-1} \leq \alpha \sqrt{n}, S_i > \alpha \sqrt{n} \\
&\qquad\qquad \text{and } S_{n_l} \leq (\alpha - \epsilon) \sqrt{n} \quad \text{for all } l) \\
&\leq \sum_{i=1}^{n} P(S_1 \leq \alpha \sqrt{n}, \ldots, S_{i-1} \leq \alpha \sqrt{n}, S_i > \alpha \sqrt{n} \\
&\qquad\qquad \text{and } S_{n(i)} \leq (\alpha - \epsilon) \sqrt{n}),
\end{aligned}$$

where in the last expression $n(i)$ means the first n_l which follows i. But note that $S_i > \alpha \sqrt{n}$ and $S_{n(i)} \leq (\alpha - \epsilon) \sqrt{n}$ imply

statement and proof we will call **Problem 2**. It is analogous to Theorem 12.2.

[17] It is a bit inaccurate to use "P" on both sides of (12), for they may refer to different measures on different probability spaces. (They might be the same too, but that would be a very special situation.)

that $|X_{i+1} + \cdots + X_{n(i)}| > \epsilon \sqrt{n}$, an event independent of $S_1, \ldots, S_i$. Thus we obtain

$$P(M_n > \alpha \sqrt{n} \text{ and } M_n^{(k)} \leq (\alpha - \epsilon) \sqrt{n})$$

$$\leq \sum_{i=1}^{n} P(S_1 \leq \alpha \sqrt{n}, \ldots, S_{i-1} \leq \alpha \sqrt{n}, S_i > \alpha \sqrt{n})$$

$$\cdot P(|S_{n(i)} - S_i| > \epsilon \sqrt{n}). \quad (15)$$

Since by definition $n(i) - i \leq n/k$, Chebyshev's inequality shows that the last factor in (15) is not more than $1/k\epsilon^2$, and so the bound

$$P(M_n > \alpha \sqrt{n} \text{ and } M_n^{(k)} \leq (\alpha - \epsilon) \sqrt{n}) \leq \frac{1}{k\epsilon^2} \quad (16)$$

is established for any $\epsilon > 0$ and any k.

Combining (13), (14), and (16) yields the bounds

$$P(M_n^{(k)} \leq \alpha \sqrt{n}) \geq P(M_n \leq \alpha \sqrt{n})$$

$$\geq P(M_n^{(k)} \leq (\alpha - \epsilon) \sqrt{n}) - \frac{1}{k\epsilon^2}. \quad (17)$$

Passing to the limit on n and using (12), we obtain

$$P(\max_{0 \leq i \leq k} x_{i/k}(\omega) \leq \alpha - \epsilon) - \frac{1}{k\epsilon^2} \leq \liminf_{n \to \infty} P\left(\frac{M_n}{\sqrt{n}} \leq \alpha\right) \quad (18)$$

$$\leq \limsup_{n \to \infty} P\left(\frac{M_n}{\sqrt{n}} \leq \alpha\right) \leq P(\max_{0 \leq i \leq k} x_{i/k}(\omega) \leq \alpha).$$

But it is clear from the continuity of the Brownian paths that

$$\lim_{k \to \infty} P(\max_{0 \leq i \leq k} x_{i/k}(\omega) \leq u) = P(\max_{0 \leq t \leq 1} x_t(\omega) \leq u). \quad (19)$$

It is therefore easy to take the limit on k in (18), follow by letting $\epsilon \searrow 0$, and obtain

$$\lim_{n \to \infty} P\left(\frac{M_n}{\sqrt{n}} \leq \alpha\right) = P(\max_{0 \leq t \leq 1} x_t(\omega) \leq \alpha) \quad (20)$$

for every α at which the right side is continuous. This proves Theorem 1. The Erdös-Kac "invariance principle" for the maximum functional is thus established in an improved form, and (1) and (2) of this section have now been fully proved as well.

27. BROWNIAN MOTION AND BOUNDARY VALUE PROBLEMS

Some of the main lines of recent research in probability concern the deep connections between Markov processes and certain parts of "classical" (that is, nonprobabilistic!) analysis. In the case of Brownian motion, these "classical" topics include especially potential theory, logarithmic in two dimensions and Newtonian in three or more, and other aspects of the Laplace operator as well. In these last two sections we will not try to develop these things systematically, but will explain heuristically two striking ways in which Brownian motion contributes to the solution of important analytical problems.

In this section we will consider the *Dirichlet problem* in the following form: Let S be a bounded, connected open set in R^k, and ∂S its boundary. It is desired, given any continuous function f defined on ∂S, to find a function ϕ which is continuous in $S \cup \partial S$, equal to f on ∂S and which is *harmonic* [18] in S. The problem can be solved in a variety of ways provided the boundary ∂S is sufficiently "nice," but there are examples in which no solution exists in the strict sense in which we have stated the problem. Norbert Wiener defined a "generalized solution" which always exists—a function which is harmonic in S, but which attains the boundary values f in a weaker sense than the one implied by continuity in $S \cup \partial S$. Wiener did not use the "Wiener process" (Brownian motion) to obtain his solution, but that now turns out to be the neatest way to do it!

We construct a Brownian motion in k dimensions by letting each coordinate function be a one-dimensional Brownian process, and making these processes independent of each other. The resulting process $\{x_t\}$ has the transition function

$$p_t(\mathbf{x}, \mathbf{E}) = \frac{1}{(\sqrt{2\pi t})^k} \int_{\mathbf{E}} \cdots \int e^{-(\mathbf{x}-\mathbf{y})^2/2t} \, dy_1 \cdots dy_k, \quad (1)$$

where $\mathbf{x} = (x_1, \ldots, x_k)$ and $\mathbf{x}^2 = \sum_{i=1}^{k} x_i^2$. If $\mathbf{x}_0(\omega) = \mathbf{u} \in S$,

---

[18] That is, ϕ is twice continuously differentiable, and $\Delta\phi = 0$ in S. $\left(\Delta \text{ will always denote the Laplace operator } \sum_{i=1}^{k} \partial^2/\partial x_i^2. \right)$

let

$$T(\mathbf{u}) = \inf \{t > 0 : \mathbf{x}_t \notin S\} ; \qquad (2)$$

because of path continuity we can say that $\mathbf{x}_{T(\mathbf{u})}$ is (a.s.) the point on ∂S at which $\mathbf{x}_t$ leaves S for the first time. Define

$$\phi(\mathbf{u}) = E(f(\mathbf{x}_{T(\mathbf{u})}). \qquad (3)$$

Then $\phi(\mathbf{u})$ is the "generalized solution" to the Dirichlet problem.

It is quite easy to see that the expectation in (3) exists; what needs to be shown is that $\phi(\mathbf{u})$ so defined is harmonic in S, and that in some sense it "takes on" the boundary values f. We will first sketch a proof of the harmonicity by a method due to S. Kakutani, who first solved Dirichlet's problem this way.[19] Given $\mathbf{u} \in S$, let B be the surface of any sphere centered at $\mathbf{u}$ and contained within S. Let $\tau(B, \mathbf{u})$ be the first time at which $\{\mathbf{x}_t\}$ reaches B starting from $\mathbf{u}$; because of continuity $\tau(B, \mathbf{u}) < T(\mathbf{u})$ a.s. By the spherical symmetry of the Brownian motion transition function, it is intuitively clear that $\mathbf{x}_{\tau(B,\mathbf{u})}$ will be uniformly distributed over B.

We now apply the plausible principle asserting that once it is known that $\{\mathbf{x}_t\}$ has first hit B at a point $\mathbf{v}$, then the (conditional) expectation of $f(\mathbf{x}_{T(\mathbf{u})})$ can be calculated as if the process began at $\mathbf{v}$; in other words it will be $\phi(\mathbf{v})$. This idea that the process can be thought of as "beginning afresh" after hitting B is a special case of the "strong Markov property" which we have also mentioned in Section 22. Accepting this, and using the uniform distribution over B of the hitting point $\mathbf{x}_{\tau(B,\mathbf{u})}$, we see that $\phi(\mathbf{u})$ is equal to the *average* of ϕ over the surface of B. This property will hold at each $\mathbf{u} \in S$ for all sufficiently small spheres centered at $\mathbf{u}$, and that fact (with boundedness, which is obvious) is enough to ensure that ϕ is harmonic in S.

The glaring logical gap in this "proof," of course, is that "beginning afresh" at the random time of first hitting B is something for which we have given no precise definition, much less a proof. We will not go into the accurate statement and proof of the strong Markov property here, but the approach above *can* be fully justified. It is, however, also possible to

---

[19] The germ of the method goes back further; it was pointed out by Courant, Friedrichs and Lewy as long ago as 1928 that random walk could be used to solve the discrete analog of the Dirichlet problem.

prove that ϕ is harmonic by more elementary, though less intuitive, methods.

We turn now to the boundary behavior of u. This is the hardest part in most of the "classical" approaches, and the probabilistic interpretation is a great help in seeing what really goes on. We begin our brief study with a very special, but illuminating case: *if S is convex, then $\phi(\mathbf{u}) \to f(\mathbf{r})$ as $\mathbf{u} \to \mathbf{r}$, where $\mathbf{u} \in S$ and $\mathbf{r} \in \partial S$.* To show this, it is enough to prove that for any neighborhood N of an arbitrary point $\mathbf{r} \in \partial S$,

$$\lim_{\mathbf{u} \to \mathbf{r}} P(\mathbf{x}_{T(\mathbf{u})} \in N) = 1. \tag{4}$$

Since f will be "almost" equal to $f(\mathbf{r})$ throughout $N \cap \partial S$ if N is small (by continuity), and is bounded elsewhere, it is easy to see that (4) implies $\phi(\mathbf{u}) \to f(\mathbf{r})$ as $\mathbf{u} \to \mathbf{r}$. This remark applies to any S, convex or not.

To prove (4) for convex S, we let p be a supporting hyperplane to S at $\mathbf{r}$. Let us choose coordinates in such a way that p becomes the plane $u_1 = 0$. Then because of the isotropic character of the Brownian transition function (1), the increments of $\mathbf{x}_t$ in the direction perpendicular to p (u_1 axis) and in directions parallel to p are independent. (This assertion takes some checking, but it is fairly easy and we will accept it without proof.) Now the perpendicular component is just a one-dimensional Brownian process, and by Theorem 22.2 (the local law of the iterated logarithm) it is clear that, roughly speaking, if $\mathbf{x}_t$ is started close to $\mathbf{r}$, and hence also close to p, it will reach p almost immediately with probability tending to one as $\mathbf{x}_0$ approaches p. In the process of reaching p, of course, $\mathbf{x}_t$ must intersect ∂S because p is a supporting plane to S. During the time $T(\mathbf{u})$, which is thus very small, the independent component of $\mathbf{x}_t$ parallel to p will have made only small progress, again with high probability, and so $\mathbf{x}_{T(\mathbf{u})}$ will be close to $\mathbf{r}$. These informal statements can be quite easily made rigorous, and they show that (4) holds at any point $\mathbf{r} \in \partial S$ where S has a plane of support. For convex sets this means all points of ∂S, and so the Dirichlet problem is solved by (3).

It is quite plausible—and true—that the reasoning used above can be extended to prove (4) and so to solve Dirichlet's problem for many nonconvex sets. Any set whose boundary is a smooth surface will do. Worse things may also be all right;

for instance, if **r** is the vertex of a cone pointing into S, in any number of dimensions, it is not hard to show that (4) holds provided the cone encloses positive solid angle at its tip.

The Brownian motion interpretation, however, also yields some insight into the possibility that no strict solution to the problem exists. For example, if the dimension of the space R^k is ≥ 3, let S consist of the open unit sphere with one radial line removed. It can be shown that if the process is started anywhere inside the sphere—even on the missing radius—the probability that $\{\mathbf{x}_t\}$ hits ∂S immediately is 0; the process acts as if it "did not know" the radius was deleted from S.[20] As a result, the values prescribed for f along the deleted radius (which is, of course, part of ∂S) have no effect upon the function ϕ of (3), and only "by accident" will ϕ tend to f at these points. It can easily be seen that no other function will do the trick either. Finally, we mention that the deleted radial line can be expanded into a sort of spine, in such a way that (4) does not hold at the tip (located at the origin). To accomplish this, the spine must come to a point exponentially fast. This example —known as a "Lebesgue thorn"—illustrates that even when the boundary of S is homeomorphic to a sphere it may contain *irregular points* where (4) fails and the generalized Dirichlet solution need not converge to the value of f at the point.

28. BROWNIAN MOTION AND EIGENVALUE PROBLEMS

In this last section we will sketch an elegant method, due to Mark Kac, by which a theorem of H. Weyl about eigenvalue problems for the Laplace operator (and some other things as well) can be derived using Brownian motion.[21] The proof will be again heuristic, but the rigorous justification of the method has been given, and some of the necessary steps will be sketched.

We will work in two dimensions for definiteness. Let S be a region bounded by a "smooth" Jordan curve ∂S, and let $\{\mathbf{x}_t\}$ be a Brownian motion process starting at a point $\mathbf{u}_0 \in S$.

---

[20] This follows from the fact (which we have not proved) that in two or more dimensions Brownian motion a.s. never returns to its starting point.

[21] It is interesting to compare Kac's method with that given in, for instance, Courant and Hilbert, Vol. 1, Chapter VI.

Define the time $T(\mathbf{u}_0)$ of first hitting ∂S as in the last section, and construct the new stochastic process

$$\mathbf{y}_t = \begin{cases} \mathbf{x}_t & \text{if } t < T(\mathbf{u}_0), \\ \Delta & \text{if } t \geq T(\mathbf{u}_0), \end{cases} \tag{1}$$

where Δ is an abstract state (not a point of R^2). We say that $\{\mathbf{y}_t\}$ is Brownian motion with an *absorbing barrier* at ∂S; the Brownian particle "vanishes" from R^2 instantly upon first leaving S, never to return.

The finite dimensional joint distributions of $\{\mathbf{y}_t\}$, like those of $\{\mathbf{x}_t\}$, are generated by a Markov transition function q_t on R^2 which satisfies the requirements of Section 23. One change is necessary, of course: $q_t(\mathbf{u}, \mathbf{E})$ is defined for $\mathbf{u} \in S$ and $\mathbf{E} \subset R^2$, but we expect that $q_t(\mathbf{u}, R^2) < 1$ rather than $= 1$ because of the chance of absorption before time t has elapsed. We saw in Section 25 that p_t, the transition function of $\{\mathbf{x}_t\}$, has for its density the fundamental solution of the heat equation, and there is an analogous fact for q_t: *the transition function q_t of $\{\mathbf{y}_t\}$ has a density $g_t(\mathbf{u}, \mathbf{v})$ which is the fundamental solution of the initial-boundary value problem*

$$\frac{\partial \psi}{\partial t} = \frac{1}{2} \Delta_{\mathbf{v}} \psi \qquad \text{for } t > 0, \, \mathbf{v} \in S; \tag{2}$$

$$\lim_{\mathbf{v} \to \mathbf{r}} \psi(t, \mathbf{v}) = 0 \qquad \text{for } t > 0, \, \mathbf{r} \in \partial S. \tag{3}$$

This is the "forward" system; the "backward" one looks just the same since g_t, like the density of p_t, is symmetric in $\mathbf{u}$ and $\mathbf{v}$.

We will not make any attempt to prove the above theorem, but just offer a few remarks to make it seem reasonable. Consider the corresponding backward problem. In this case both (2) and (3) are rather plausible. The point is that the backward diffusion equation can be derived much as in the unrestricted case treated in Section 25, using two-dimensional analogues of (25.5)–(25.7). These are the same as for unrestricted Brownian motion because the boundary has little effect over very short periods—the probability of reaching ∂S from $\mathbf{u} \in S$ in time $[0, t]$ is $o(t)$. Moreover, if the Brownian process starts very near ∂S, it is plausible that the probability of "surviving" until time t will be nearly 0, and so (3) should hold. When the backward system is known, the forward one can be obtained from it since the transition function is determined; the theorem above is the result.

It is well known [22] that the fundamental solution of (2) and (3) can be expressed in terms of the eigenvalues λ_n and the normalized eigenfunctions ϕ_n of the system

$$\tfrac{1}{2} \Delta\phi + \lambda\phi = 0; \qquad \phi(\mathbf{u}) = 0 \quad \text{if } \mathbf{u} \in \partial S. \tag{4}$$

Since the fundamental solution is also (we have asserted) the transition density for $\{\mathbf{y}_t\}$, we obtain

$$g_t(\mathbf{u}, \mathbf{v}) = \sum_{n=1}^{\infty} e^{-\lambda_n t} \phi_n(\mathbf{u}) \phi_n(\mathbf{v}). \tag{5}$$

We will use some very plausible considerations about $\{\mathbf{y}_t\}$, together with (5), to study the λ_n and ϕ_n.

The "principle of not feeling the boundary" asserts that

$$g_t(\mathbf{u}, \mathbf{u}) \sim f_t(\mathbf{u}, \mathbf{u}) = \frac{1}{2\pi t} \qquad \text{as } t \to 0; \tag{6}$$

the function f_t is the transition density for the unrestricted Brownian motion with no absorbing barrier. The idea behind (6) is that the transition probabilities in the immediate neighborhood of the starting point are little affected by the boundary at first, until the process has a chance to reach the boundary and return (or, in the case of $\{\mathbf{y}_t\}$, to fail to return). It is noteworthy that $g_t(\mathbf{u}, \mathbf{v}) \sim f_t(\mathbf{u}, \mathbf{v})$ holds even when $\mathbf{u} \neq \mathbf{v}$, provided the line segment joining $\mathbf{u}$ to $\mathbf{v}$ is contained within S (Ciesielski). In a case such as the one in Fig. 2,

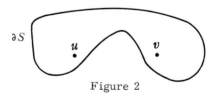

Figure 2

however, it is easy to see that transitions from $\mathbf{u}$ to $\mathbf{v}$ are significantly affected by the absorbing boundary no matter how short the time period.

[22] See Courant-Hilbert for discussion. Formally, it is clear that the right side of (5) below has the desired properties.

The use of probability in this approach to Weyl's theorem is completely contained in (6). The argument above makes this relation seem quite plausible, but probabilistic considerations can contribute to its rigorous proof as well. For instance, it is "obvious" that

$$p_t(\mathbf{u}, \mathbf{E}) \geq q_t(\mathbf{u}, \mathbf{E}) \qquad \text{for all } \mathbf{u} \in S, \mathbf{E} \subset S,$$

since the presence of an absorbing barrier can only reduce the possible ways of getting from $\mathbf{u}$ into $\mathbf{E}$. It follows that q_t is absolutely continuous, with a density less than that of p_t. To obtain an inequality in the opposite direction, we construct a square containing $\mathbf{u}$ and included in S. If this square is made into an absorbing barrier, the transition probabilities for the resulting Brownian process starting from $\mathbf{u}$ will be even smaller than those for $\{\mathbf{y}_t\}$ (that is, q_t), since absorption takes place sooner. These probabilities, however, can be calculated explicitly by elementary arguments and (6) verified for them; hence g_t is "sandwiched" by functions obeying (6) and must do so itself.

Combining (5) and (6), we have

$$\sum_{n=1}^{\infty} e^{-\lambda_n t} \phi_n{}^2(\mathbf{u}) \sim \frac{1}{2\pi t} \qquad \text{as } t \to 0 \tag{7}$$

for each $\mathbf{u} \in S$. Integrating both sides over S yields formally

$$\sum_{n=1}^{\infty} e^{-\lambda_n t} \sim \frac{A}{2\pi t}, \tag{8}$$

where A is the area of S. The left side of (8) may be written as a Laplace-Stieltjes transform:

$$\sum_{n=1}^{\infty} e^{-\lambda_n t} = \int_0^{\infty} e^{-tx}\, dF(x), \tag{9}$$

where $F(x)$ is the number of eigenvalues λ_n which are less than x. We can now appeal to Karamata's Tauberian theorem,[23] which relates the asymptotic behavior of the Laplace transform

[23] See Widder's book, Chapter V, Section 4.

at 0 with the growth of F at $+\infty$. Using (8), the result is

$$F(x) \sim x \frac{A}{2\pi}. \qquad \text{as } x \to +\infty. \qquad (10)$$

An equivalent statement, in view of the definition of F, is

$$\lambda_n \sim \frac{2\pi n}{A} \qquad \text{as } n \to \infty. \qquad (11)$$

This is Weyl's theorem.

We have also almost derived a later result of Carleman. Let us return to (7) and treat it as we did (8) above, without even integrating on $\mathbf{u}$. The analog of (10) is

$$\sum_{\lambda_j < x} \phi_j{}^2(\mathbf{u}) \sim \frac{x}{2\pi} \qquad \text{as } x \to \infty, \qquad (12)$$

which is Carleman's theorem.

The point of this section and the last one is not to provide simple proofs of hard theorems, for by the time all gaps are filled it is doubtful if very much has been gained over "classical" methods. It is hoped that some new intuitive insight has been provided. But the main moral is that there are deep connections between certain probabilistic models and some branches of classical analysis, which can, and have, led to profound enrichment of both fields.

Bibliography

BOOKS ON MEASURE THEORY

[H] P. R. Halmos, *Measure Theory*, New York (Van Nostrand), 1950.
[M] M. E. Munroe, *Introduction to Measure and Integration*, Cambridge, Massachusetts (Addison Wesley), 1953.
[R] H. L. Royden, *Real Analysis*, New York (Macmillan), 1963.

OTHER BOOKS ON ANALYSIS

(These were referred to in Chapter 4 for special topics.)

R. Courant and D. Hilbert, *Methods of Mathematical Physics* I, New York (Interscience), 1953.

S. Kaczmarz and H. Steinhaus, *Theorie der Orthogonalreihen*, New York (Chelsea), 1951.

D. V. Widder, *The Laplace Transform*, Princeton, New Jersey (Princeton University Press), 1941.

BOOKS ON PROBABILITY

(Books for which no description is given have
been mentioned in the text.)

[Do] J. L. Doob, *Stochastic Processes*, New York (Wiley), 1953.   An advanced treatise devoted to the theory of all the major types of stochastic processes.
[Dy] E B. Dynkin, *Markov Processes* I, II, Berlin (Springer), 1965.
 [F] W. Feller, *An Introduction to Probability Theory and Its Applications*, Vol. I, New York (Wiley), 1957 (2nd ed.).   This is an outstanding introduction to the subject of probability, at a fairly elementary mathematical level (premeasure theory),
[F2] W. Feller, *An Introduction to Probability Theory and Its Applications*, Vol. II, New York (Wiley), 1966.   An elegant sequel to the first volume, it gives among other things a thorough

144

treatment of sums of independent random variables, with many applications and examples. Over 600 pages.

[G] B. V. Gnedenko, *The Theory of Probability*, New York (Chelsea), 1962.

[GK] B. V. Gnedenko and A. N. Kolmogorov, *Limit Distributions for Sums of Independent Random Variables*, Cambridge, Massachusetts (Addison Wesley), 1954. This monograph is the most definitive work on the "central limit problem."

[IM] K. Ito and H. P. McKean, *Diffusion Processes and Their Sample Paths*, Berlin (Springer), 1965.

[Ka] M. Kac, *Probability and Related Topics in Physical Sciences*, New York (Interscience), 1959. This interesting book contains sketches of a wide variety of special problems and applications of probability theory. It makes a good companion to any more conventional, systematic text.

[Kh] A. Khintchine, *Asymptotische Gesetze der Wahrscheinlichkeitsrechnung*, New York (Chelsea), 1948.

[Ko] A. N. Kolmogorov, *Foundations of the Theory of Probability*, New York (Chelsea), 1956. This classic short monograph, first published in 1933, has played an important role in the development of the subject. In the course on which the present book was based, [Ko] was used as a text for the portion devoted to foundations; the essentials have here been incorporated in Chapter 1.

[Kr] K. Krickeberg, *Probability Theory*, Reading, Massachusetts, (Addison-Wesley), 1965.

[Le] P. Levy, *Processus Stochastiques et Mouvement Brownien*, Paris (Gauthier-Villars), 1948.

[Lo] M. Loeve, *Probability Theory*, Princeton, New Jersey (Van Nostrand), 1964 (3rd ed.). An advanced general treatise, including a nice short text on measure theory.

[S] F. Spitzer, *Principles of Random Walk*, Princeton, New Jersey (Van Nostrand), 1964.

[Y] A. M. Yaglom, *An Introduction to the Theory of Stationary Random Functions*, Englewood Cliffs, New Jersey (Prentice Hall), 1962. This monograph gives a nice treatment of a class of stochastic processes of great importance in many applications.

SELECTED ARTICLES MENTIONED IN THE TEXT

Section 7

[1] E. Borel, "Les Probabilités dénombrables et leur Applications arithmétiques," *Rend. circ. Math. Palermo* **27** (1909). (Of historical interest.)

Section 12

[2]   Yu. V. Prokhorov, "Convergence of Random Processes and Limit Theorems in Probability Theory," *Theory Prob. Applications* 1 (1956), pp. 157–214.

Section 13

[3]   B. V. Gnedenko, "Sur la Distribution limité du Terme maximum d'une Série aléatoire," *Ann. of Math.* 44 (1943), pp. 423–453.

Section 19

[4]   K. L. Chung and W. H. J. Fuchs, "On the Distribution of Values of Sums of Random Variables," *Mem. Amer. Math. Soc.* 6 (1951).

Section 22

[5]   A. Dvoretzky, P. Erdös, and S. Kakutani, "Nonincrease Everywhere of the Brownian Motion Process," *Proc. Fourth Berkeley Symp.* II, University of California Press, 1961, pp. 102–116.

Section 24

[6]   J. R. Kinney, "Continuity Properties of Sample Functions of Markov Processes," *Trans. Amer. Math. Soc.* 74 (1953), pp. 280–302.

Section 25

[7]   A. N. Kolmogorov, "Uber die analytischen Methoden in der Wahrscheinlichkeitsrechnung," *Math. Ann.* 104 (1931), pp. 415–458.
[8]   W. Feller, "Zur Theorie der stochastischen Prozesse (Existenz und Eindeutigkeitsatze)," *Math. Ann.* 113 (1936), pp. 113–160.

Section 26

[9]   P. Erdös and M. Kac, "On Certain Limit Theorems in the Theory of Probability," *Bull. Amer. Math. Soc.* 52 (1946), pp. 292–302.
[10] M. Donsker, "An Invariance Principle for Certain Probability Limit Theorems," *Mem. Amer. Math. Soc.* 6 (1951). See also paper [2] for the most comprehensive treatment.

Section 27

[11]   S. Kakutani, "Two-Dimensional Brownian Motion and Harmonic Functions," *Proc. Imp. Acad. Tokyo* **20** (1944), pp. 706–714.

Sections 27 and 28

[12]   M. Kac, "On Some Connections between Probability Theory and Differential and Integral Equations," *Proc. Second Berkeley Symposium*, University of California Press, 1951, pp. 189–215.

[13]   M. Kac, "Can One Hear the Shape of a Drum?" *Amer. Math. Monthly* **73** (1966), No. 4, part II, pp. 1–23.

Index